Hannes Taugwalder

The Lost Valley

Hannes Taugwalder

The Lost Valley

An autobiographical tale

Verlag Glendyn AG Aarau

As the 20th century draws to its close, we look back through the mists of time to its early years. When life was more leisurely, although not easier, when we really did have time to "stop and stare".

Zermatt, the tiny village resting at the foot of the all-dominant Matterhorn. Zermatt, the spiritual home of so many British mountaineers, and, tragically, the last resting-place for some.

Hannes Taugwalder, son of a mountain-guide, descendant of one of Zermatt's great mountaineering families, writes in this his first autobiographical novel, a tender, humorous and vivid account of life as a member of a simple peasant-farming community. Hannes Taugwalder is a born story-teller, and those of us fortunate enough to know him closely can easily visualise his twinkling eyes, twitching moustache and throaty chuckle as he writes about his boyhood.

"The Lost Valley" has been overwhelmingly successful both within Switzerland and beyond its borders. It has already been translated into French, and is in the process of being filmed by a Swiss television company.

"The Lost Valley" appeals to a wide audience: the elderly who remember with affection their own childhoods, the lovers of Zermatt in all its seasons, whether hikers, mountaineers or skiers, and last but not least those of us who only «discovered» Zermatt in relatively recent times, but by whom its charm and mystery are nonetheless treasured.

Inhaltsverzeichnis

Prato Borni (Introduction)

My forefathers were mountain farmers. They had the carefree hearts of shepherds. Their home was not the bottom of the valley, but the slopes lying around the Matterhorn. There they grazed their herds and eked out a meagre living. But their isolation was not loneliness, nor their poverty a misfortune, for they were free men. Their short lives were a passage to the eternal pastures. Nature alone set the rhythm by which they lived.

If they found it difficult to write a letter or draw a realistic picture of a goat, they built their own houses, baked their bread, wove their cloth; they knew the healing herbs, could play a sprightly tune on the fiddle and send a merry yodel pealing across the valley. They depended only on the weather and their animals. They got on well with their mules, and walked with them down to the Rhone valley, earning the nickname, in dialect, of "d'Seimini", the mulers.

The Bible may have told them to "make the earth subject unto ye", but they smiled at such ideas. They did not think much of that. Their relationship to nature was a brotherly giving and taking. They were simple hill farmers, no more. But another biblical injunction: "Grow ye and multiply" they certainly took to heart!

Trees were sacred to them. No tree needed a preservation order. All the trees were preserved. Even the most decrepit withered pine would be cut sparingly. Only dry branches, stumps and roots were used for firewood and burned in the kitchen ranges and stone stoves. In the mornings a bluish, aromatic haze of woodsmoke often hung over the roofs of Zermatt. The chainsaws did not yet sing their rasping song of death in the forests.

They fetched irrigation water from the glaciers and gorges in long channels, hanging wooden troughs, from steep cliff faces to bring the precious liquid down to the arid meadows and little fields. Without the water grass would not grow on the slopes exposed to the sun.

With their two or three cattle and a few sheep, goats and hens they followed the good grazing land. In spring they went up the mountain to the district of Aroleid, living with their animals in the little village of Zumsee until the pasture bloomed. The animals spent the summer on the alpine pastures at Hermetje, Stafelalp or Kalbermatte. Where the lush grass grew, the men built simple huts, grazed their small herds and, when the frost came, returned to the valley.

Cash was something they seldom saw, a necessary evil that they kept at arm's length. Self-sufficiency was what mattered. It alone made a man free. And freedom was everything to them. That's why they planted even the smallest field with potatoes, rye, broad beans, cabbage and beet. Milk, cheese and butter were their staple diet. The meat hanging in the storage barns was home-killed. It was only served at table when the stocks allowed it.

My father was proud to call himself poor. He would tease the rich farmers at every opportunity:

"Josi, you know the difference between the rich and the poor?"

"The rich have got it and the poor want it", laughed the tight-fisted farmer with toothless malice. He came from the nearby village of Blatten.

"That's right," my father replied. "And they've got it because they sell their full-cream milk to other people and serve skimmed milk to their own families."

The Blatten man did not like such talk.

"Rich or poor, they're all the same before God," he snapped. "We all have to work with our own hands in this world. Who do you think carts the dung to my meadows? I dug over ten fields this spring. Moved the earth two feet up the mountain because the cold winter had shoved it down."

My father laughed: "You're working yourself to death. We don't need to overwork ourselves.

"When the hot days come round I have to carry hay-bales into the barns till I look like a hunchback."

"You look like one anyway," my father joked. "But still, at least you can have a tipple whenever you like."

"You manage that as well, once in a while."

The man from Blatten was seldom short of a repartee.

"I'm glad I do. Otherwise the folk down there could send for me straight away."

Father crooked two fingers into a pair of horns and pointed at the ground, where the imps lived deep below. They both laughed.

Men who thought much of themselves would get a little drunk from time to time. That was part of being a man, like the long moustache, the fat watch-chain, the battered hat and a few patches on their trousers. It would have been a poor sort of fellow who never had a glass or two! They didn't ask for much. New soles on their shoes once a year. A white woollen scarf for Mother in autumn. Now and then a new exercise book for the children. A packet of spicy tobacco for the old folk – and all was right with the world. What else did anyone need? Money would always be short in any case. Father kept his modest savings in a wooden cigar box in the bureau, to which he had the only key. Mother had to ask him for any little thing she wanted to buy. Such was the custom.

But the wheel of time did not stop turning even in our valley at the world's end. It turned faster and faster. We never stopped having surprises. The first policeman, the first doctor, the first railway and the first electric light appeared. Strangely, they all came at the same time, together with uniformed hotel staff, the dealers in fruit from warmer climates, and the souvenir shops. A new age dawned. The age of tourism, technology and progress, of mountain railways, corrugated-iron roofs, telephone poles, asphalt, advertising signs and buses. The epoch of "sacred" climbing began, when the mountains were held in almost religious awe. My forefathers became completely addicted to it. To lug a heavy rucksack into the mountains, to tackle a virgin peak or take a new, untried route with an ice-pick in your hand, a lead-rope slung over your shoulder and an eccentric Englishman in tow – that was the ultimate delight. The mountains, which they had regarded up to then with a certain suspicion, suddenly took hold of them like a drug.

But all was not well with this new world. People were too dependent on chance, the basis of their livelihood was too precarious. My grandfather often had to cut the bread so thin that daylight shone through when you held it to the window. And my grandmother died in great pain with no doctor present. Our stores, too, were always used up by spring. When the first guests arrived at our little tea-room, our hearts fluttered more joyfully than the Swiss flag on the roof. A few coins found their way into Father's money-box, and Mother dug a bit deeper into the sugar sack.

First Confession

The village priest had prepared us for weeks for our first confession. I was by now convinced that never before had God's earth brought forth such a degenerate, sinful creature as I was, and was not likely to do so again. I had offended not once but repeatedly against the Ten Commandments of the Lord and the Five Commandments of the Church.

With my precisely quantified burden of mortal sins and a total of venial sins beyond any power of computation, I stood one late afternoon before the confessional with other young miscreants, who all had to confess for the first time. This great washing of souls did not take place in the nave, but in a crypt below it, a room like a catacomb, into which a dim light filtered through painted windows. There was an atmosphere of penitence spiced with sighs and the hardly audible whispering from the confessional. The altar stood in front of the middle window, whose painted panes showed the Mother of God stricken with grief. On her lap lay her son, with the Crucifixion wounds, pale, bloodless, lifeless – all because he had had to die for our sins.

To brood over the question why Jesus had to die in advance, 2000 years before our sinful doings, would have inevitably led to further sins, and even one of these, unconfessed and unrepented, would have been enough to buy a ticket to one of the lowest platforms of Hell, where there was weeping and gnashing of teeth to the end of time. This irrevocable damnation did not, to be sure, assort easily with the kind, fatherly God we encountered in our lessons. However, it was not for us to understand God, but to love, fear and worship him. Especially fear.

During a lay mission a Capuchin friar depicted what it was like in Hell so vividly and realistically that the men shuffled their hobnailed boots and the women tied their headscarves tighter under their chins. Only my father commented after the sermon, a knavish gleam in his eye: "He must have been down there himself."

"Seven metres thick are the walls of that place of eternal horror, behind which the blazing flames of hell lick the souls of wretched sinners without burning them up, scorching them until the Day of Judgement and for ever after that. Everlastingly! – If a jackdaw were to whet its beak once each year on the rock of the Matterhorn, and each time sweep away a little grain of rock from the mighty mountain, some time in the reckoning of eternity the day would come when the mountain would have been levelled by the jackdaw's beak. But on that day eternity would have just begun! Therefore sin not. Do penance! Guard yourselves against fleshly lusts and let your hearts not cleave to earthly dross!"

While he was stoking the fires of Hell a few degrees hotter from the pulpit, an avalanche thundered down past the snow-bound village into the valley, taking a few stables and barns whirling with it and burying cattle and sheep under masses of snow. "The Lord hath given. The Lord hath taken away. Praised be the name of the Lord." And the congregation said: "Amen."

My sinful behaviour had begun at the age of five, perhaps even earlier. And it began with the very Commandment that caused God special aggravation: Thou shalt not commit adultery. Someone who knew better had reworded it to say: Thou shalt not be unchaste. Our priest, who was a very close associate of God's, knew that the slightest thought that consciously dwelt on an impure subject was an unforgivable offence to God. And the concept of impurity covered everything between the shoulders and the knees. Only the unconscious thought that flapped above your head like a crow was not sinful.

In my case the crows circled above my head for a disgracefully long time, cawing with fleshly lust. Of

12

course, the sins of youth are especially sweet. The excitement prickles in your fingertips. But just before you go to confess them, ears drooping before the confessional as you scrape together your many misdemeanours and try to recall the exact number of times – the excitement prickles a good deal less.

Little Grete, who was, so to speak, the *corpus delicti*, was present too. She knelt in her pew like a little bundle of misery, hiding her face in her hands. Had she spied between her fingertips and seen me, she must have wished me on the lowest of all platforms of Hell. And not without reason. I was the guilty one and was ready to confess it, and accept all the penitential prayers. Maybe my friend Alex, the same age as me, shared the guilt. Who could know for sure, apart from God, who registered such things with the utmost care? Alex and I had persuaded Gretchen to come into our living-room. Our parents were working in the fields. The wind howled in the chimney. When the Foehn died down in the village, you could still hear it groaning in the pine and larch woods in the mountains. Then it was backrubbing itself on the corner of the house, caterwauling like a lovesick tomcat. The priest shut his windows, the village schoolmistress her blouse and the street-sweeper his beer-bottle. Only the old folk opened their mouths. They couldn't draw breath. The Foehn drove me too to distraction. I was in a state of near delirium, as if I had eaten too many bilberries or drunk too much wine. The air outside the window was an almost violet blue. The mountainsides seemed to nudge closer to the houses. A confusing, unreal atmosphere enveloped the village.

Perhaps the Foehn had also brushed across the Holy Land when our Lord was tempted by the Devil on the pinnacle of the Temple. If you fall down and worship me, I will give you... Was there anything the Evil One hadn't promised? We can't possibly know everything – only those who were present heard it, the lies, the deception, the temptation.

Sins often start with a lie. Alex and I had told little Grete some big ones. About the treasures hidden under my parents' bed, with stood on tall wooden legs in the corner of the living room. Access to the spot was veiled by the long fringe of the handwoven blanket, which also dimmed the light. Too much light is always a nuisance to sinners. Did little Grete really believe in the hidden treasures when she crept with us under the fringes and lay stretched out on her front? Or had the little Foehn devil grabbed her too with sweet childish desires? She let us fold back her skirt and slip down her panty, revealing to our avid eyes the glory of the world, her velvet-soft bottom. We brushed across the tense orbs with the palms of our hands. Nothing we had ever done could compare with this.

True, it all looked very different from in front of the confessional. Then you had to reconstruct exactly how often your hand had brushed across.

"Did you also look at it?" That too I had done, infamous creature that I was.

"And deliberately thought about it afterwards?"

How could I not? That made my position so much the worse. But that was by no means everything.

We boys often tried to arch our water over a high fence. Some had evolved a very effective technique. No fence was too high for them. Another special honour was to cast one's stream the furthest from the top of a wall, instead of modelling oneself on Saint Aloysius, whose statue stood on the side-altar in the crypt. He held a lily in his hand and looked up to the ceiling through his halo. We had strict instructions to appeal to him at the very first stirring of sensual lust, as, for example, when the little devil used a caprice of the wind to lift the girls' skirts, billowing them out and revealing long, bare, shining thighs. Why had the Lord afflicted us with so *many* sensuous joys? Just a little dark curl on a pretty woman's neck aroused sinful lewdness in the most steadfast man.

14

Married men could permit themselves to put their hands on the bosoms of their grown-up daughters. And it was quite natural for them to make demands on their legitimate wives up to three times a day: on waking up, after lunch and during the long evenings. No wonder the extended families were bursting at the seams. Too many children lost their mothers too early. Who knew better about the reasons for all this than the father confessor? But no blessing and admonishing made any difference. He blessed bed and board, stable and barn, power station and railway, folk-dance and alphorn-players, the graves of young mothers – and the re-marriage of widowers. He thundered from the pulpit, rubbed the congregation's noses in their sinful lives, adjured them to take the pictures of the saints out of their bedrooms and mountain huts to spare the saints at least the sight of their ill-doing. But it made no difference. The people turned up at mass, took the sacrament, and went on sinning as before. Over and again the priest had to acknowledge that despite the lay mission, the Easter sermon, the spiritual exercises and all the grace dispensed by the sacraments, his congregation got no better. He was often discouraged, but comforted himself by thinking what his flock would be like if they were left to Satan without his help. This gave him strength to renew the struggle.

Through the grating inside the confessional I saw the priest's snow-white hair. His purple stole glimmered in the half-light. I pressed my remorseful nose against the bottom of the wooden lattice. Above my head, where the adults posted their big missives to the beyond, the wooden slats were discoloured, as if singed by the many sins.

"Seventh Commandment. Thou shalt not steal. I hope you've done better in that department."

"No, I've stolen too. Sugar beet. At least three handfuls."

"Did you return them?"

"My father birched my bare bottom for it."

15

"That was quite right. But you still have to give back the beet."

"But we haven't got any beet. We never have."

"Then you must work to pay them off. Help the farmer with his sowing, weeding or haymaking. Do you understand? – Why don't you answer me?"

"Yes."

"Yes what?"

"I'll do the haymaking."

"Is that all?"

The venial sins and the Church Commandments still had to be broached. "These and all the other sins of my life I sincerely repent. I earnestly seek to be better. I beg for holy penance and absolution."

I was dismissed with the *Ego te absolvo* and the advice not to offend the Lord with any more sins.

With the great abasement behind me and feeling myself a worthy candidate for heaven once again, I left the confessional with a light heart and went happily up to the nave. The penance prayers were said in the nave. I reeled off two or three extra "Our Fathers" just to make sure.

From the vaulting God the Father, with his white beard, dressed in oriental robes and adorned with crown and sceptre, looked down benevolently on the small, repentant sinner. Above him the Holy Ghost in the form of a dove fluttered along the ceiling, while Christ was depicted as the Lamb of God in the arch of the vault. The Lamb held a banner, the sign of victory, in its front hoof. From its breast a stream of blood poured without overflowing into a chalice. Behind its head a rainbow arched like a halo. I was reconciled with the Holy Trinity. Entirely its child once more. That was as it should be. All was right with the world again. – But life went on.

In the tavern

Uncle Arnold, who had lived in the flat above us since he had been widowed, had finished washing up. You could hear every step he took. Ceiling and floor consisted of a single layer of boards. Father hadn't yet come home. There was only a piece of larch-root glowing in the stove. But the noodles and potatoes left over from lunch, which were simmering in the frying-pan, had become dry and hard. Mother would wait no longer. With the usual advice on how I was to behave in an inn she sent me into the village to remind the reveller about his supper.

It was a rather delicate mission. A wrong word or ill-judged behaviour could easily spoil his best mood. I hated this "Going-to-fetch-Father", but my elder brother had found a job on the tunnelling site at Amsteg with Uncle Petermartin and was no longer at home. My sister was unsuited to the task. One did not send girls into pubs. So, with the usual protests, I set off reluctantly.

The naked bulb of the single street lamp swung in the November wind, shedding a ghostly light on the narrow lane that led down to the village. I glanced furtively into all the unlit corners and open cellar doors. The main street was better lit. I wondered which pub to start with. The one I hated most was the Café du Pont. It stood on the right bank of the stream – the Triftbach – near the church square. Everyone coming from the upper village had to pass it. Including, of course, old men with parched throats. A lot of spirits were drunk there. You could smell the brandy when you walked past.

The inn windows were misted up. It was already as cold as winter. Icicles hung from the river bank, and there were thin sheets of ice over the puddles. They crunched under your feet. It was impossible to recognise the figures behind the dim panes. I stopped outside the door and tried to make

17

out the voices, but the rushing stream drowned the noise from the inn. I hesitated to go in. The Café du Pont could be called the dregs of the Zermatt pubs. The notorious drunks of the village met there. Suddenly someone wrenched open the door. A staggering figure made its way behind a wall near the street to pass water. The inn had no sanitation. There was a sour smell of drink and urine. In the tobacco haze I recognised the figures at the different tables. Father was not there. Relieved, I made for the next pub, which was on the church square.

To reach it you had to climb a few steps up a massive stone staircase. The door of this inn had glass windows. A corner of the bottom window had broken out. I pressed my nose to the door and peered through. I heard Father's voice coming from a knot of chattering figures, telling some anecdote. Then I saw him. He was sitting at a table in the corner, in the best of spirits. Old men were sitting there with their hats on. That was the custom. Only when they met the priest or the village doctor did they touch the brim of their hat, bending it up slightly. They knew what respect was due to whom. The hat was only taken off in church, or in bed. In the pub it stayed on. According to mood it was worn either on the back of the head or pulled down in front. Father was wearing his tilted somewhat back. A good sign. I went in.

Father had light-blue, mischievous eyes. His banter twinkled in them long before it passed his lips. Then the creases beside his eyes would fan out like a spider's web towards his ears. He was especially good at teasing women. You could actually read his thoughts from his face. His blond moustache was copper-coloured towards the middle, tinged by the pipe smoke that rose constantly before his face like a fair-weather cloud. When he told a story, he kept his pipe in his mouth. Puffs of smoke swirled from the bowl in elaborate patterns. He had had a turbulent life and was a good raconteur. And he always had friends who listened. Most were simple, sociable souls who enjoyed a good glass of wine.

Father was anything but a drinker, but it happened now and then that he got stuck in one pub or another and lost track of time.

Auctions of land and property were always an occasion for a general drinking session in the village. These public auctions were always held at inns. Free wine flowed in plenty, to bolster the bidders' courage. The rage and lamentations over the over-generous bids came with the hangover next morning.

Only when the mood in the pub had reached the proper pitch was the first small stub of candle lit. The usher started with the sale of the old mill by the river:

"What am I bid?"

"Five hundred!"

"Burning for Bärenfeller Anton. Who'll offer more?"

All eyes were on the candle, that was still burning vigorously.

"Five hundred and twenty."

"Burning for Rüden Alois" – it being the custom in our region to say the surname first.

No-one showed much inclination to bid any more. The flame began to flicker.

"Five hundred and thirty."

"Burning for Thamatter Peter. – The mill's worth·twice as much! Who bids more?"

The flame turned bluish. It flickered violently two or three times, fighting for its life. My father shouted:

"Five hundred and fifty!"

"Burning now for Seimi Rudolf." That was what they called my father. Everyone was staring at the flame. It leapt up once more, then it was all over. Thamatter Peter had managed to call out five hundred and sixty, but it didn't count. The offer came too late. A wisp of smoke stretched from the wick to the ceiling. The mill belonged to my father. As he went out he had said to my mother:

"Wonder who'll buy the old mill by the Triftbach."

"Not you, I hope! I wouldn't know what to do with it. And we'd have no money to pay for it."

"Of course not," my father replied edgily. Mother had had a worried look as he left.

If Father had been a rich man, he would have enjoyed auctions more than anything. As it was, he was usually just an onlooker. Now he scratched his beard and furrowed his brow. Those who knew him realised he was wondering how he was going to pay for the mill. He had no use for it. It backed on to our henhouse and was a romantic little building, but we had nothing to grind.

"Now you own the whole strip of land between the Triftbach and the Gletscherstrasse," someone said.

Rudolf nodded absently.

"We must drink to that!"

"What's that? – Oh, yes. Of course. Zischga, another litre and four glasses."

So the drinking started again. No-one had eyes for the clock as it got dark and the women and children waited at home with the steaming soup.

I slowly shut the door and stood in the midst of all these men. They looked at me amiably enough. The sexton was there as well. He shouted something to me that I couldn't understand. There was laughter at his table. It was like the school playground. Only the innkeeper's wife was giving me an unfriendly look. She was afraid I might remind the other men too about going home. She decided to go on the attack:

"Rudolf, your wife has sent your little boy for you. Looks like it's your bedtime."

This was an unfair humiliation in front of his colleagues. Father was anything but a henpecked husband. It was only now that he noticed me. He gazed at me thoughtfully with

20

his light-blue eyes. I tried to smile and sat down beside him without a word. There was only room for half of me on the bench.

Mother had advised: "Don't draw attention to yourself. And please don't say he should come home. He'll remember. Do you understand?"

Of course I understood. Children understand more than grown-ups like to believe. But I couldn't know that the landlady would try to provoke him.

For a moment the pub went quiet. The men were waiting for Father's reply. Then, thank goodness, old Fenner's cracked voice was heard, raised in a wheezing song. It was right out of tune, and some people started laughing, but he was undeterred. As he warmed his theme, he was joined by other, more tuneful voices.

My father joined in too. It was a foreign song the mountain guides had heard in the Dolomites. It had been sung a lot lately, and ran something like this:

> Oh when I've done living
> Done living, done living
> Six maidens with zithers
> shall carry me thither
> So I'll always be happy
> be happy, be happy
> and God rest my soul.

I couldn't understand how my father could sing such rubbish. His eyes were shining. He beamed at the thought of such a funeral. Lifting his glass, he sang at the top of his voice: "So I'll always be happy, be happy, be happy."

Sitting at the next table was an old scarecrow of a man they called "Bayi". I couldn't look at him, or he would have come to father's table. No-one wanted to have anything to do with him. He was a down and out of the worst kind. You couldn't tell where he was looking, his watery eyes squinted so badly. If one eye pointed at the ceiling, the other would be looking out of the window. He talked to himself, raised his empty schnapps glass to his lips and tipped it back. Then he got angry when nothing came out. He flung his arms about and shouted as loud as his quavering voice was able: "Zischga, gimme... drink! You hear me... stupid bitch!"

Zischga sat like a fat spider behind the counter, watching all her victims. She took not the slightest notice of old Bayi. Anyone who had run out of money did not exist for her.

At the next table there were a number of mountain farmers. Two were arguing about irrigation water. They had their land at Aroleid and belonged to the same watering commune. Old Thamatter was waving his finger threateningly in front of Bärenfeller's nose: "You won't take my water away from me like that again, I promise you... sure as I'm standing here." Actually he was sitting. He must have drunk some "bad" wine. According to Mother: "There's bad wine and good wine. When men drink bad wine, they get bad-tempered and quarrelsome." She was right. Thamatter had drunk some bad wine. Otherwise he wouldn't have been in such a bad mood. I knew the old man. He would never hurt a fly. The landlady began to fear that fists were about to fly. She sat down with them and smoothed things over. She filled their glasses. The men agreed on another half-litre of white wine, and the thunder-clouds rolled away.

Most of them had their wives and children waiting at home. Perhaps milk and water were having to be added to their gruel to stop it boiling dry.

"Six maidens with zithers shall carry me thither."

It was a sin to sing such a song – it was blasphemy! A cold shiver ran down my back. Dying is a serious matter. I had seen Uncle Joachim die. He had opened his mouth wide and fought against the end with his whole body. His mouth had to be tied shut afterwards with a cloth. How often I had looked on when dead people were lifted from their beds into their coffins. The windows had to be opened because there was a strange, dizzying smell. Sometimes their lips opened, showing the yellowish teeth like a fixed grin in the pale, sunken face. A lifeless body was always horrifying. And the funeral! It was anything but a procession of happy zither-playing maidens. It was a deadly serious matter with the cross and flags, holy water and tolling bells. Behind the black coffin walked weeping women and children, with the priest praying aloud and uttering beseeching words. When the ground was frozen and the priest sent hard lumps of soil drumming down on the coffin lid, no eye stayed dry. "Thou art dust, and unto dust thou shalt return."

"So I'll always be happy, be happy, be happy, and God rest my soul."

How could my father enjoy singing such a song? Did he really think Mother would walk grieving behind his coffin if six zither-playing maidens carried it down to the churchyard? She'd send those women packing and help carry the coffin herself, if no-one else would do it. Father was usually so sensible. When he showed me how to dig big tree-stumps out of the ground, since they made such excellent firewood, he was a real master.

I had to help him saw and split wood. I was allowed to cut wild hay with him, glaze windows, mend kitchen chairs and tables and look at the animal book he had brought back from India, which was kept locked in the chest like a jewel. And now I had to sit beside him in the smoke and listen to him blaspheming about death with his friends. What a stern look God the Father must have been giving him when He saw this. I looked up at the smokestained ceiling. Hanging near the ceiling in a black frame was a picture that I always found disconcerting. A young couple was parting, for ever I supposed, before a cross hung with flower garlands in a forest clearing. The way the man stood with his hunter's hat in his hand hinted that fate was stronger than their love. She covered her tear-stained face with the tip of her petticoat. She must have been from a good home. She wore such fine clothes, while he was a man dogged by fate. Perhaps a poacher. Or was he something worse? You know how reckless young men can be. Or was he just poor? So poor she couldn't have him? Probably he wasn't good enough for her father. Fathers always have something against their daughters' loves. When my sister went to a forbidden dance at a neighbour's house, Father beat her with a birch rod. Tears came to my eyes. To see so much of love's sorrow in one picture was heartbreaking.

"And maidens with zithers." I got up. I'd had enough. "Yes, son, you go home," said my father, "I'll follow in a minute." So he wanted to stay. So be it. I nodded to his companions and left. It was important to be nice to his friends. And he would surely have come if Zischga hadn't teased him. Old Fenner patted me on the shoulder. There was a mischievous smile in his eyes. Perhaps he'd remembered the sugar beet I had stolen from him. I'd had to spend a day haymaking with him in the summer to make up for it. He gave me as much bread and cheese as I could eat, and fresh milk from a bucket, still warm from the cow, in the evening. The account was settled. "Don't wait up for me," Father called after me. "I'm not hungry anyway, just thirsty – devilishly thirsty!" Everybody laughed. Father's ship was back on an even keel.

Mother was disappointed when I got home. "All right, let's eat," she said, scraping the dry remnants from the pan.

We had hardly started eating when we heard steps on the flagstones below the stairs.

"He's coming," said Mother. The steps sounded first on stone, then on the wooden stairs. Irregularities and interruptions indicated that the climber was having difficulty. On the first landing, which led off to the rocky slope the house was built against, he paused to relieve himself, looking up meanwhile at the night sky to assess the weather. Then an erratic climb up the second flight of stairs. The front door flew open, banging against the wall. Then came heavy footsteps along the passage to the kitchen door. Father stood in his patriarchal grandeur in the doorway, blinking affably and intoning: "The mill-wheel be turnin' right in the mill-stream, clip, clop. – Behold the Miller of Triftbach!" We all laughed. – "It's not clip, clop," I corrected him, "but plip, plop."

"You hear that, Mother? Teacher says it be plap-plap, clap-trap. That be right, Teacher, bain't it?"

I couldn't see any more. My stomach ached from laughing. Even Mother had to sit down on the kitchen bench. "Ah, I see you're laughing at me. All right, that's the last time I sing with you, that is." He sat down at the table. Mother tried to offer him the food. "No, I don't want anything to eat. Just something to drink. Not that stuff! Get me a strong coffee... but with something in it... you understand? I haven't seen a drop of alcohol all day." And he laughed at his own wit.

Water-wheel

Father started taking an interest in the flour that Mother kept in a square tin box in the kitchen. This was quite new. He took a teaspoonful of it and rubbed it between forefinger and thumb. At breakfast he took a long look at the slice of bread he had just cut. His bright-blue eyes shone with satisfaction: "We'll soon have flour from our own mill."

Mother laughed out loud: "How will you manage that without grain? – Perhaps using pebbles from the Triftbach?"

Father refused to let such quibbles spoil his mood: "I'll hire out my work as a miller. Not for money. For goods. That's what the farmers want." The corners of Mother's mouth quivered, but she held her peace. She could not share his pleasure in buying the mill. She had no hopes for it. Her dream was a small guesthouse. She saw herself in the kitchen, providing for the bodily well-being of her guests. Lina could be the chambermaid and Father the porter. But Father would have none of this. Being a hotel servant did not appeal to him. When they married, she had persuaded him to leave Zermatt for the winter and work together at the Hotel Château du Louvre in Menton, he as the hotel doorman.

The first shoes he cleaned for a guest were put back outside the door. There was a difference of opinion between him and the guest. Finally, some trouble with the hotel management that was only put right with Mother's help. No, he was not suited to the hotel business. "I gladly leave that to people more gifted for it than I," he laughed.

Father now owned his own mill and was well pleased. After all, it was not any old mill. It had a horizontal water-wheel. What the advantage of that was over a vertical wheel we did not understand. It was enough that Father knew. He was the miller.

When the first attempt was made to set the mill in motion, there were a few surprises. The horizontal water-wheel lost half its paddles. Some were rotten. Others fell from their slots and disappeared in the swirling water of the Triftbach. It was a thoroughbred, our mill. Not like the rattletrap of the village baker!

And it was easy to have a soft spot for a small, old mill close to the rocks into which the stream had worn a secluded alcove overhung with dog-roses and gnarled larches. Sun and spray had dyed the wooden beams silver-grey. The roof of mossy stone slabs sloped down towards the stream. Three steps led down across worn boards to the low, slightly arched doorway.

Father had something of the adventurer in him. He saw himself as the miller looking on while the water-power did the work, the grain rippled between the millstones and the white flour flew into the box.

He loved the wild sound of the water with the mill-wheel beating time. Wasn't that much like the trombone parts he played with the village musicians, or the rhythm he gave the polka and waltz in the ländler dance-band? Could he wish for anything finer than to look out of the little mill window into the stream that caught his dreams in its water and bore them off on new voyages while the old mill did its duty?

Reality didn't prove quite so straightforward. In the first days Father often stood up to his ankles in water. Measuring for the new paddles, he caught a cold. For many people a cold is an inconvenience. Not for my father. He was never ill, but a cold reduced him to abject misery. Mother fetched a bag of throat-tablets with a honey filling from the village shop. "Especially suited to colds and sore throats", the packet said in black and white. Father sucked a couple of them and declared they were no use. Mother urged more patience. This is just what the invalid lacked. "The only thing they help is the shopkeeper's purse", he grumbled, reaching for the bottle of home-made remedy. Mother laughed. He sloped off sullenly to his workbench and made six new paddles.

A stonemason was engaged to cut new grinding surfaces on the heavy millstones. The whole mechanism was overhauled. Mother scrubbed out the big flour box and scoured the old wooden floorboards. Spiders, woodworm and daddy-longlegs were swept from the walls.

Then came the great day. A farmer provided my father with two sacks of rye for a test grind. Naturally without payment. He was taking a certain risk, after all.

The sluice was opened. The water sped down the wooden troughs over the rocks. The old mill trembled. Slowly the horizontal water-wheel under the floor began to turn, setting the whole mechanism in motion. The mill had awakened to new life. Its clatter drowned even the raging stream. Windows opened in the neighbouring houses. Everywhere were happy faces, delighting in the new noise that rivalled the din of the river.

More and more people came to the mill. Father and the rye-farmer presided over the bustle. They took flour samples from the box with little wooden shovels. They were both well aware of the importance of their task and full of praise for the quality the first test had demonstrated.

True, at that moment Father was unaware that it was also to be his last commission as a miller. The village baker was not prepared to bake bread with flour that did not come from his own mill. Father heard of this only a few days later from the rye-farmer, who was stuck with his flour. This effectively diverted the water from Father's mill, though the Triftbach raced past just as noisily.

But my father had his moment of glory on that single day of milling. There were so many people present that they trod on each others toes. Father sent Rudolf and me out.

We could not understand that the very people who owned the mill or were to inherit it one day had to hang about outside.

We climbed about in the rocks and turned our minds to the water-troughs. When we tossed in plant leaves, they turned instantly into a green streak, the water shot down so fast. Bark or twigs only changed the colour of the magic effect. We wondered what the water would do with stones, which lay around in such profusion and in so many sizes. The little stones disappeared altogether. There was a plume of spray when they went in, then a thud from the paddles as they reached the bottom. But nothing happened. So we needed bigger stones. I had a heavy, well-rounded, slippery rock in my hands. I could hardly lift it into the trough. I had to turn it round till it fitted. The water spurted from the channel like a fountain. Then the stone vanished like all the others we had thrown in, and the mill shook with a splitting crash as splinters of shattered paddles flew into the stream.

We made off behind the chicken run. Peering through a dogrose bush, we saw Father's face appear in the doorway. His eyebrows and moustache were white, his hair and shirt snowy as if he had just climbed out of the flour-box. He looked up at the stone slabs of the roof. We saw no more, thinking it better to seek safety in distance. Rudolf ran home to Mother. I sauntered down to the village square.

As we found out at supper, Father had first thought the turmoil in the mill had shaken a roof slab loose. But an inspection had shown that the roof was intact. But as the wheel had been damaged all the same, he assumed there must have been a stone left in one of the channels. He cursed himself for not checking them more carefully.

Luckily, he said, this had happened after they had finished the milling test. Rudolf and I looked hard at the gruel we were diligently consuming.

Big Agatha

On the south side of Fabian's House, in the village square, there were two weather-worn logs. On them sat a number of men who had no work. They warmed themselves in the sun. And because the day was long, they passed it by teasing the villagers who passed with scythes, pitchforks, baskets and suchlike implements. Sometimes they managed to find someone gullible enough to believe their stories.

"The priest's looking for you! Your goat's got into his vegetable garden and eaten all his lettuce."

Since his boy had passed by with a goat a short while before, the farmer believed them and rushed to the parsonage. The men enjoyed their little joke. So the time was passed in excellent spirits. As I came along, one of the loafers called:

"Hello, Hannes. Off to ring the bells, I suppose?"

A stupid question. On an ordinary weekday, when everyone was at work. There was really no reason to ring the church bells. So I said, a bit nonplussed:

"Me? No I'm not."

"Just what I thought. You're not big enough."

"He can't reach the ropes yet, poor little mite", jeered another.

"I've already helped the sexton", I retorted.

"You hear that? He's already helped the sexton!" He whistled through his teeth. I could see they were poking fun at me and was not going to let them get away with it.

"Yes, I dare say you've rung the little bell once or twice. But not Big Agatha. To take her on you've got to have something here."

He showed off his biceps.

"I've rung Big Agatha too. – I did it with a school friend."

"Well, with two of you there's nothing to it. But you can't do it on your own."

"You wouldn't get a sound out of it, I bet you whatever you like."

"Course not. Take a look at him. Hasn't got what it takes."

"If I wanted to, I could make Big Agatha ring. – But I don't want to."

"Why not? Are you scared?"

"No, but it's sacrilege."

They all laughed. "Sacrilege? Now what might that be?"

"I don't know either. It's got something to do with the Church and God. I think it's something like a mortal sin with consecrated things."

"Leave the little chap alone," said someone. "He's afraid of the priest."

"I'm not afraid of the priest!"

"Course you are. You're yellow!"

"I'm not yellow."

"Then show us you're not."

"He's yellow all right. Just take a look at him."

"No, it's not true!"

"All right, either you prove you're not, or you're just a little yellow-belly."

"You see? I told you so. He's not up to it."

"All right, I'll do it – But if you tell on me…"

Threats were out of place, I could see that.

"Who's going to tell on you? Us? We're men of honour, all these gentlemen here."

They laughed at the idea of being called gentlemen. It was just the kind of joke they enjoyed.

"The kid's going to sound the fire alarm. The whole village will get a fright. They'll come running from the fields, terrified they're losing all they've got. Wonder how long it'll take the first fireman to get here? We could get out the pipes and ladders ready for them."

A barrel of fun for men hanging around bored, with their empty hands and not much else in their pockets. And that on a day when the Foehn was slinking down the alleys, squeezing between the skinny houses with their touching roofs, whipping up a little tongue of flame in the hearths. The loungers would poke their noses into everything.

Perhaps spread a rumour: "There's a fire in Getwing, I've heard," or somewhere else, just to build up the uncertainty. They raised their self-esteem from pranks like this. Naturally, they didn't want to ring Big Agatha themselves. That would have been ridiculous, even for them. They needed a boy to do it. Some proud little blighter daft enough to be provoked. I was just right. Someone who wanted to be an officer and a mountain guide could not afford to be called a yellow-belly.

Such a person really wouldn't have what it takes. It was working like a charm.

I went to the church porch and swung open the heavy door. An elderly woman was kneeling at the tenth Station of the Cross, sunk in her meditations. She paid no attention to me. Along a side-aisle I reached the short stone staircase that led up to the door of the bell tower. Four ropes hung down from the tower to the floor. You could ring the bells either here or up in the bell loft.

Through the side door I could see the everlasting light flickering on the altar. It reminded me the living God was very close indeed. The Almighty was locked up in the fireproof, burglar-proof tabernacle on the Baroque altar, lonely and spinning out His time in those unenviably cramped quarters. All the same, it seemed advisable to close the door to the choir.

I knew my way about the ropes. I knew the one that swung Saint Agatha. What I didn't know was that the priest was reading his breviary behind the church, and that his cook was weeding the graves in the nearby churchyard. I hung on the rope with my whole weight. It hardly moved. You had to let it go, then immediately pull it again, to get the bell slowly swinging. Once the rhythm was going, it was easier to pull in time.

Up in the tower the beams of the bell-cage creaked and groaned. The rope hissed softly in the concrete holes. Otherwise there was eery silence. With all my strength I heaved the rope.

Then came the first dull boom from above. A short pause, then again the clapper struck the bell. There followed three regular peals, though not all equally loud. But between the chimes I heard the lock of the sacristy door turning. I knew what that meant. Letting go of the rope, I ran up the short tower staircase, then jumped out of a small side window into the street. Just at that moment the cook was coming back from the churchyard. I ran straight into her arms.

"Aha, you're the little pest. Father's going to be very pleased with you," I heard her scolding. There was no point in making off for the Lower Village, as if it was there, not in the Upper Village, that the sinner should be sought. She'd recognised me.

The men of honour didn't have quite the fun they were hoping for. A few windows were opened, some people climbed on to their roofs, and enquiring looks were sent from the fields. But nowhere above the steep gables was a puff of smoke to be seen. The chimes had no clear meaning. They were too short and hesitant for the fire alarm, which was sounded with quick beats of the clapper, not by swinging the whole bell. Nor were the few chimes enough to announce a service.

Mother was surprised at my eagerness to spend a free Wednesday afternoon doing homework. But it wasn't long before a knock came at the front door. In stepped the man of the cloth in person. He stood in front of my mother in his long, black cassock and told her he would like to speak to his new sexton. This sexton had rung the bells for an afternoon service and then fled from the church. He, the priest, would like to hold the service and needed the sexton's help.

Without saying a word I got up from the table and went to stand red-faced beside the priest. Mother gave the clergyman an understanding look. "What? Hannes did that?" She tried to look stern, but not very convincingly.

I had to walk beside the priest down the main street to the church. The people we met knew what all this meant. They could tell from my crestfallen look. They laughed and passed their comments. In the square the men of honour were still lounging. So they were to have a little fun after all. They raised their hats and respectfully wished us a "pleasant evening." And asked if it was really time for the rosary service already.

For an hour I knelt before the side altar on which Jesus stood to his full plaster height. On the Baroque folds of his robe flamed his gilded heart, to which he pointed insistently while his other hand sketched the question: "What have you done to me?" Now and then I stole a furtive look at his kindly face with its well-trimmed beard, busily mumbling my rosary prayers.

After an hour of this the priest came back. He sent me home with helpful admonitions. I never again officiated as a sexton; but my enthusiasm for prayer was not increased. I expected a well-deserved punishment from Father when I got home. A healthy tanning of my bare backside with a birch rod, as was the custom with us. It didn't happen. Father saw the funny side of the affair. He'd never have thought I would ring the bells in the middle of a weekday afternoon just so that I could spend an hour praying by myself in the church, he declared cordially.

Convent life

Every year the priest of Turtmann received a few bottles of altar wine from the convent of Sainte Vierge. No doubt a very pious custom, but not quite as disinterested as it might seem. The gift contained a tacit reminder of the service the priest was able to render the convent from time to time. This consisted in spelling out to some deserving girl the many spiritual benefits of the convent life.

My mother's parents lived in Turtmann, a pretty village in the plain of central Valais, not far from the border with the French-speaking area. The village's few houses and its stately church were crammed against the steep, shadowy side of a gorge.

Barbara, my mother, was undoubtedly a deserving girl. The priest noticed how devoutly her snub-nose approached the communion rail. She sang the hymns with fervour. In the religious education lessons she could answer the questions on the sacramental sources of grace and the one true faith exactly as the book said. No wonder the priest thought her well suited to the life of the cloister. And there were already quite a number of empty bottles in the cellar.

Grandmother and the spiritual gentleman were soon of one mind. They did not talk of the nun's life, but of the good convent school that could smooth a clever girl's way to everything she would need in later years. French, housekeeping and gardening, the convent virtues – in short, everything that made life rich and full.

Little Barbara's chestnut eyes shone at the thought of these opportunities. In this way the good little girl, seen through the glowing bottles of fine altar wine, took on the secret aura of a future nun.

The Reverend Mother of the convent of Sainte Vierge soon noticed that the new girl from Valais was made of the right stuff. Just as she liked young aspirants to the cloister to be: cheerful, pious and obedient.

Barbara did not find it difficult to fit into the new community. She loved the night services with the old hymns that sounded as if they came from another world, and the candle-light and the haze of incense. Hadn't she been on first-name terms with all the saints even when she was still at home? And the work in the kitchen, the laundry and the garden made a welcome change after the lessons, which concentrated on religion and languages. In short, she was quite happy in her new surroundings.

It was hardly surprising that the Reverend Mother soon offered her the novice's habit. From that day on Barbara moved about the old rooms in the ankle-length, charcoal-coloured convent dress. Although she was impressed by her own dignity, she could not get used to her new role. She kept her long stride, her cheerfulness and her mischievous tongue. In the playground, when the supervising nun was not looking, she would give the ball a forbidden kick, although she already had to regard herself as something like Our Lord's betrothed.

To become a true bride of Christ she still lacked – apart from greater age and deeper religious knowledge – practice in the virtues and rules of the order, the oath and the bridal ring, a privilege reserved for the impressive ceremony which was to crown her education.

Barbara dutifully tried to practice humility and to lead a life pleasing to God. The Reverend Mother knew what pleased God and what did not. She was omnipresent like the Almighty, praising and blaming, admonishing and consoling, embodying the traditions and rituals and the ancient rules of the order. These demanded no less than the complete abandonment of a personality of one's own. "Learn to endure the wrong done to you in humility. Praise the hand which unjustly chastises you. Never forget the words of Our Lord: If someone strikes you on the left cheek, turn the right."

It was this renouncing of oneself that defeated Barbara. The rule of self-mortification was her undoing. She could easily sympathise with all the virtues: charity, help to those in need, obedience and purity. She liked the many prayers and services. All this seemed a sensible way to attain eternal bliss. But to accept injustice with humility, and then say thank you, went against her nature. She felt it was beyond her.

Why don't they ask us to fight against injustice? If necessary, to use our fists to defend justice, as often happened in our native valley? Why not risk your life to right a wrong instead of accepting it? That would make much more sense. She no longer understood the values that were being applied to her, and began to doubt her calling. Then something happened which changed the direction of her life. Each Monday some of the novices had to scrub the convent's bed-linen on washboards at an enormous tub in the laundry. Barbara like this work. The girls could sing, giggle and gossip as is the habit of regular washerwomen. True, they had to sing holy songs. But even these allowed them to give vent to some of their inner feelings. Claudia, a girl from the Freiburg region, of whom Barbara was especially fond, was also there.

Suddenly the Reverend Mother came in. Striding purposefully up to Claudia, she scolded her for the untidiness of her cell. The bed was not made. The floor looked like a pigsty. The books were all over the place. And someone like her wanted to be a bride of Jesus! Passing Claudia's door, Barbara had glanced in although the girls were not allowed to visit each other's cells. Everything was as tidy as could be.

Claudia was dismayed by the unexpected accusations in front of the other girls. She blushed, looked down and with Christian humility asked to be justly punished for her negligence.

The moment she heard this Barbara forgot the washtub. She stood up. If the Reverend Mother had looked, she would have met the blazing eyes of the young girl from Valais. But then Barbara went back to rubbing the sheets with her fists, smacking the sheets on the board so hard that the water splashed far and wide. The Mother Superior became aware of Barbara's excessive zeal. She bade her not to be overenthusiastic. For God loved moderation in all things. Barbara would have liked to give her the same advice, but thought it better to defuse the issue by thanking her for her good counsel. But afterwards the memory nagged. "Do we have to put up with everything?" she wondered. "That can't be what our life is for!" He doubts about her vocation grew stronger. She could not put the idea of leaving the convent out of her mind, but how she was to put this into practice she did not know.

The convent grounds were enclosed by a high wall. The gate was always locked. All incoming and outgoing letters were opened. On Sundays all the novices trotted like good little ducklings two by two to the village church. They were escorted by three sisters. To smuggle a letter out of the convent bordered on the impossible. And yet she needed her mother's help. She would never manage it on her own.

Saint Anthony

Barbara no longer prayed for a life pleasing to God. She formed a pact with a saint she particularly revered, St. Anthony, putting all her trust in his help. "He's bound to think of something," she told herself encouragingly. "He's never failed yet."

Barbara had some past experience of dealing with the holy man in the brown habit. She now had a kind of barter in mind, a deal with a guarantee. You made a sacrifice or a promise so that you would afterwards get what you wanted. The saint always honoured such agreements, Barbara knew that. So she was quite prepared to make a down payment.

She went more often than before to the small chapel in the convent garden to press her case before the saint's statue. The Mother Superior took this as a sign of increased piety in her novice and applauded her zeal. But St. Anthony was in no hurry to offer his help. Being used to heavenly chronology, he kept people waiting on earth. Barbara complained to him about this.

Through the open door the wind swept around the chapel, threatening to blow out the candle Barbara had lit on the altar. Overcome by self-pity, she knelt at a pew and saw the saint's kindly face through a blur of tears. He smiled benevolently from the altar in the flickering light, while she argued the justice of her cause. "What else must I promise to make you get on with it?"

On the very day Barbara's trust was most deeply shaken, the saint finally consented to act. As so often he made use of an accident, which really wasn't an accident at all, since something very peculiar – accidentally – happened.

While Barbara was struggling to see through the tears flowing copiously from her eyes, something dressed in white fluttered to earth between her and the saint. "An angel!" she thought. "He's sent me an angel!" She almost fainted with rapture. She could clearly hear the voice of the airborne creature. But she could not comprehend the revelation. It had a strange sound, not like something from the Beyond. Unbelievably, it was more like... clucking. Barbara had to blow her nose to get a clearer view. At this moment the saint intervened. He said in a deep voice – she heard it quite clearly, it was no hallucination: "You damned creature." Barbara was shaken to the marrow.

She'd never expected to hear the saint use such language – and he was talking Valais dialect. How could he say such a thing! Her mother would have boxed her ears. Again her eyes filled with tears.

Only now did she notice someone with a green apron in the doorway, which she had left open – a man who obviously didn't know how gardeners were supposed to behave in church. One of his hens had strayed in. Ought he to boldly fetch it out, or let it enjoy the sanctuary of the holy place? Barbara did not know whether to laugh or cry. She was completely confused. But she knew one thing: someone had just spoken in Valais dialect. Timidly she approached the convent gardener: "Are you from Valais?" she asked in tentative vernacular. The old man nodded: "Aye, from Agaru, that I be."

"I'm from Turtma," Barbara went on.

"Then thee be Barbara Zbru, ain't thee? Many a letter I've brought thee from the post. I know thy mother really well, I do."

To Barbara this came like a message from a different world. The hen was making its panicky way between the pews. Then they heard it clucking in the garden.

"God be with you," the gardener said, and was gone. Barbara could hear him trying to coax the hen.

For a while she stood rooted to the spot. Then she knelt down, filled with joy. The miracle had happened. Anthony had sent her a helper. She showered the saint with her profusest thanks. Now it was up to her.

From this day on Barbara always carried a letter in her bodice. It was addressed to her mother and contained all the woes she had stored up inside herself. It closed with the fervent plea that her mother write to the Reverend Mother to say she was ill and urgently needed her daughter to nurse her. "But of course, only if you still love me and want me back home." She knew this last sentence would move her mother's heart.

Barbara planned to pass this momentous letter to the gardener when the opportunity arose. She counted on him not to misuse her trust. "He's sure to take it to the post, not give it to Reverend Mother," she told herself, "He's from Valais, too." To her in the foreign surroundings of the convent that was the same as having a member of her family nearby.

But the opportunity would not arise. The letter withered on her bosom. Finally, it was the reverend lady herself who gave her unwitting help.

One evening she ordered Barbara to lock up the chickens. By day they were allowed to roam freely in the yard and garden, but because of the martens they had to spend the night in the hen-house with the window shut. When Barbara counted them, they were all installed dutifully on their perches asking only to be left in peace. Barbara shut the window. Then she noticed the gardener in the nearby kitchen garden. This was her opportunity. But it demanded the utmost caution. How did she know that the Mother Superior's stern gaze was not fixed on her from behind the windows that reflected the vivid light of the setting sun? There might be a hen still missing. She pretended to look for it. With loud cries of "Chicky-chick-chick" and other such endearments she approached the vegetable garden. As she passed near the old man, she pushed the letter at him with words of entreaty. She saw him look at the address, then stuff the letter into his apron pocket. She took that as a good omen. "He won't betray me, I know he won't," she assured herself.

Barbara was having a language lesson when there was a knock at the door and the Mother Superior came in. She whispered to the nun who was teaching. Barbara then had to follow the reverend mother to the refectory, not knowing what this might signify. The Mother Superior seemed deeply concerned. "Unhappily, I have bad news for you", she began.

"Bear it with Christian fortitude. You mother is very ill. She urgently needs your care. You must leave us for a while. Isn't that sad?" And indeed, there were tears in her eyes. Barbara too began to sob. The weeks of uncertainty had overstretched her nerves. Now she shed tears of relief and secret joy.

"We shall pray to St. Anthony," the Mother Superior went on, "that your mother will speedily recover and you can come back to us." Barbara nodded submissively. Things were beginning to get complicated for the saint. How he was to cope when asked for opposite outcomes to the same situation Barbara did not know.

In clothes that had grown too small for her during her stay she strode back through the convent gate into worldly life. In her little straw basket she carried her few earthly possessions and under her bodice a joyous heart. She had turned her back on the order's rule: "Bear injustice with humility" in order to face the many injustices of life. But isn't life also something that never works out as planned?

The meeting

Barbara's mother was overjoyed to have her daughter home again: "I didn't know the convent had such strict rules, otherwise I should not have sent you." Thus she excused herself. "But your manners are better." Barbara laughed: "No! I'll never learn good manners," and she sang from morning to night as she did the housework.

Less delighted about Barbara's return was the village priest. He scolded her for having left the convent in such an inglorious way.

"You'll have reason to wonder why you turned your back on the heavenly life," he warned with raised forefinger. Barbara reminded him about their talk about the convent school. "There wasn't any mention of being a nun then. But I might have become one if they hadn't taken the convent virtues so deadly seriously," she answered mischievously. All the same, she sometimes felt slightly guilty for her white lie, which must have offended God.

In the village she had to give an account of herself and her departure from the convent. You don't become a novice and then run away. Some people even claimed she had been expelled for impropriety with the convent gardener.

"Maybe," she laughed. "I'm just not as pious as you are. That's why I won't be a nun," she said with a touch of spite.

As chance would have it, a neighbour who worked in Zermatt during the summer received a letter from the owner of the Stafelalp Hotel, a Frau Viktorina, asking him to find her a particularly hard-working girl.

"I thought of Barbara at once, "he told her mother.

"This Viktorina – is she a nice woman?" asked the mother.

"Not just a nice woman, a nice lady," her neighbour replied self-importantly.

"And what is my daughter to do for her?"

"Wait at table! Well, that means doing the rooms as well. And washing up. And helping in the kitchen."

"Isn't that rather a lot?" asked Barbara's mother with concern.

"It's a small hotel, a guest house, you know. In a place like that you have to put your hand to everything."

Barbara liked the suggestion. "Yes, Mother, I should like to work in a hotel. I'd enjoy it."

"There's something else though," the neighbour cautioned. "The hotel is right at the end of the valley, directly below the north face of the Matterhorn. Practically at the end of the world, where the foxes and rabbits say goodnight to each other. What I mean is, it's pretty lonely. Not much for a young girl to do."

"Oh, don't worry about that. She's just come out of a convent. Much better if there's not too much to do," Barbara's mother replied.

"Fine, then everybody's happy." Our neighbour was visibly relieved. Everyone shook hands, and it was all settled. No-one mentioned wages, working hours or holidays. These were incidental. What mattered was to find work. Such details could be agreed on when you had shown what you could do.

A week later Barbara was on the Stafelalp. Frau Viktorina ran a simple mountain guest house. The few rooms contained only iron-framed beds. Next to the bed was a bedside table with a candlestick. All the rooms were lit by candlelight, even the kitchen with its large wood-stove. There was wood and water in plenty. The water was fetched from the nearby stream. In front of the guest house stood some rickety tables and chairs. They were very simply made and told of the hard winters they were exposed to in front of the house.

Barbara set to work eagerly. From early morning till late at night she was busy about the house. New jobs kept appearing for her. She hardly gave herself time to eat.

Viktorina was delighted with her industrious helper, treating her like her own daughter.

The landscape made a deep impression on Barbara. The gnarled pines, marked by their battles with the storms, appealed to her. Under the trees carpets of alpine roses stretched across the slopes. Around the guest house, too, countless alpine flowers trembled in the fresh wind from the glaciers. Barbara could not look up at the north face without a tingle of fear.

"How can anyone climb such a mountain? It's tempting God's patience to the limit", she decided. She gave a slight shudder. Some ice that had broken away from the Tiefmatten glacier was thundering down the rocky lower slopes of the Matterhorn.

Through her bedroom window she often looked across to the other side of the valley. The Kalbermatte pasture with its two cowsheds and its tiny hut – an oasis from another world amid the shadowy rocks. The little buildings crouched against the sheltering cliff. The projecting meadow, enclosed by a semicircular wall, looked like a large green pool; the rest of the pasture showed all the colours from burnt sienna to slate grey. A few sheep grazed the strips of grass between the rocks. Barbara watched a shepherd who must, she thought, have spent the night in the little hut. Viktorina wouldn't believe this: "No, no-one spends the night in the hut. It's haunted. He wouldn't live to see the morning!"

"I'll go over and have a look at it," said Barbara.

Viktorina laughed: "It's so small there isn't even room to make love in it."

There was a knock on the shutters. New guests had arrived. An English mountaineer and a guide from Zermatt sat down in the sun. They wanted refreshments. The visitor ordered a cup of tea, the guide a glass of *Fendant*, the local white wine. As Barbara poured it for him, his light-blue eyes met hers. She smiled in confusion and the glass overflowed.

"Now what have I done," she apologised with a slight blush. She didn't usually get confused so easily. The guide swept the spilt wine to the floor with his cupped hand.

"Nothing to worry about," he said with a laugh. Barbara gave him a timid glance. As she walked to the door, she noticed he was still looking at her. She observed the tourists through the kitchen window. And as the two mountaineers crossed the moraine of the Zmutt glacier a short while later, she was standing in front of the house looking after them with the empty glasses in her hands. The guide had turned round twice to look back at the hotel. She had seen it quite clearly. A smile flitted across her face. She hurried to Frau Viktorina in the kitchen.

"Who is that guide who drank Fendant with the Englishman?", she asked.

"Aha, you seem to like him," Viktorina teased. "He's called 'Seimu Rudolf'. He's a widower. His wife died in church on Candlemas day."

"In church?"

"Yes, during mass. Simply dropped down dead."

"That's really tragic. He's still so young!"

"Yes. She left him with a child."

"Are you sure you're talking about the right one? The one with the blue eyes and the ginger moustache?"

"Oh yes, I'm sure he's the right one," said Viktorina, smiling meaningfully. "Now, Barbara, take those gentlemen their soup – even if they haven't got a guide!"

Barbara took the bowl to the wrong table. She noticed her mistake.

"I'm doing everything wrong today," she complained.

Viktorina was wearing an amused smile: "I can tell you something else about him. He's travelled halfway round the world."

This is how my parents met. A year later they were married. Father could not have found a better wife. She was the kind of companion he needed. Barbara did not look for her own advantage. She followed her heart. She said Yes to a life with an adventurer who brought a sickly boy into the marriage. And also Yes to the many burdens destiny held in store for her.

The bed

The old houses of Zermatt cowered lower and lower under their stone slab roofs, dwarfed by the new arrivals. Architects were singing the praises of box-like hotels, tin roofs, brick buildings and asphalt roads.

Our house stood near the Triftbach. Like most Zermatt houses it contained several apartments. The stairs ran up the outside walls. We lived on the second floor. At the back the building was sheltered from wind and storms by a rocky wall. Most of the windows faced the sun. Above the three living-room windows was painted a yellow trombone, signifying that my father was an enthusiastic trombonist of the village band.

The furniture was very simple: the kitchen stove, the dining table and my parents' bed were the three most important items, the stone stove and the corner table in the living-room were necessary extras, and the two wardrobes and the sideboard in the kitchen were luxuries. A few nails in the walls served as clothes pegs. On a meathook in the hall hung the rucksack, the *chamma* (a mountaineer's carrying-frame with a rope), and an old guide's rope. Behind the somewhat forwardleaning pictures of saints were a number of books and calendars. Then there was Father's writing desk, where he kept documents and contracts. He set great store by a good bed. In it the children were conceived and brought into the world. He being responsible in the first case, Mother in the second. In this bed he also hoped to die, well-prepared for the long journey.

Then the bed would be free again for the next generation. That was why a good bed was important.

Its size was fixed in advance, like the shape and length of the coffin. In all the houses the bed stood on its massive wooden legs in the south-west corner of the big room that served both as living-room and the parents' bedroom.

Powerful, almost exuberant, it stood staring into the room with its many knotty eyes. Had it not been consigned to a corner, it would no doubt have got up to all kinds of mischief, so much was it a part of the family.

It wasn't a proper double bed. Father and Mother had to lie close together to have enough room. If Father bent his legs, Mother had to bend hers to fit. And if he turned over, she had to follow suit. Only with outstretched legs was there enough room. Grandfather had made the bed and given it to Father for his first marriage. At the foot end a low, narrow bed could be slid between the tall legs. At night this was pulled halfway out. It allowed the numerous babies to be accommodated where their breathing could be heard.

Uncle Caesar's bed had bandy legs. You had to suppress a smile when you saw it. It looked ridiculous, standing awkwardly in the corner and sulking. Aunt Magdalena had a neat little bed. She was not married and lived in a simple one-room flat. Her fiancé had made it before he had a fatal accident as a mountain guide. He had gone up on to the Leiterspitze with a mentally unbalanced alpinist who was seeking death in the mountains. It was a heavy blow to poor Magdalena. He had left her behind, alone with the bed. If anyone had needed something more than just the bed, it was Aunt Magdalena. The bed stood teasingly in the corner of the room, putting out its delicate little goat's legs below the bright bedspread she had knitted herself. It was a very peculiar bed. A kind of big cradle, a cradle for two grown-ups. There were no pious pictures hanging beside it, as it was the custom. My parents had the Sacred Heart of Jesus and the Virgin Mary above their bed, behind glass in gold frames – insipid, sentimental reproductions with flaming hearts drawn on their breasts. A crown of thorns encircled Jesus's heart. Mary's heart was pierced by a sword. Both were bleeding. Jesus looked piteously into the room, while Mary looked up at the ceiling in sorrowful rapture.

49

Aunt Magdalena had a picture of the penitent sinner Mary Magdalene hanging over her bed. As I looked at her with her long dishevelled hair and her almost seductive beauty, my aunt said roguishly: "She was a naughty girl as well, you know."

"A naughty girl? Isn't she a saint?"

Aunt Magdalena noticed that I didn't understand: "Listen, my lad. When you read the Bible, you have to imagine it as if it were happening today. People have always been people and always will be. They were no better in the old days, and won't be in two thousand years."

"The priest said you know good people by their deeds", I replied.

"You know who are the good people when you are alone with them. Up in a pasture or a forest, or in the dark. Believe me, I could tell you a few stories. If you have to go through life alone, like me, you get to know what people are like – I mean men. Those pious churchgoers suddenly start singing a very different song!"

"You women are not all angels either," I countered.

"What do you know about women at your age? The worst woman is a hundred times better than the best man. A man is never capable of genuine love. I admit, my fiancé was an exception. We women are different. Mary Magdalene washed the Saviour's feet with tears of repentance and dried them with her hair. After that she never left his side. She followed Jesus when he was dragged up Calvary like a criminal. That was a woman! It's in the Bible. You can read it if you don't believe me. Now do you understand why I want to have this picture over my bed?"

"Of course – but why was Mary Magdalene a naughty girl?"

Aunt Magdalena's face lost its frown. He eyes shone. A merry laugh escaped her: "You know, Hannes, to understand that you'd have to be a Magdalene yourself!"

She sat down on her bed with its little goat's legs, smiled and ran her palm over the bedspread. Her chestnut hair fell over her shoulders. Would she dry someone's feet with it too, I wondered to myself.

That evening I could not get to sleep. Aunt Magdalena's stories and my mother's worries about the buying of the mill had unsettled me. I lay in bed. The streetlamp, swinging in the wind, cast alternating light and shadow on the ceiling. The dark knotty eyes in the ceiling boards stared at me, then vanished again in the dark. The game went on endlessly. The door to my parents' bedroom was open. Father came up into this next room from the kitchen with a heavy tread. He felt for the switch and turned on the light. With considerable trouble he took off his clothes, hung them over the chair, put out the light and fell into bed. The mattress squeaked and groaned. Then I heard a hearty yawn.

Mother was still down in the kitchen. She had finished the washing-up and hung the frying pan on its nail. A long dull gong-sound boomed through the rooms. Soon after, I heard Mother's tired steps in the next room. She undressed in the dark, chatting with Father till she got into bed. Father always wanted the outside berth, although Mother came to bed after him and had to get up very early in the morning. It didn't disturb him when she scrambled over him into the corner. If he was asleep, it didn't wake him. He always had a deep, healthy sleep.

I heard her creep into bed and settle down against the wall. Suddenly there was a dreadful noise, as if the bed had collapsed. There was a thump against the wooden wall. I sat up in fright and listened. I didn't know whether Mother was crying or complaining. I wanted to rush into my parents' room, but then I heard Father laughing. "Get off, please," Mother groaned. "You're hurting me; I'm squashed." Father laughed: "I can't. Really!"

The base of the bed had slipped off its support on the wall side and fallen to the floor. On the other side it was still fixed to the frame. On this sloping surface Mother slid into the angle between wall and bed and Father rolled on top of her. He thought it a huge joke. Mother could hardly move and found her position anything but comic. It took some time for Father to climb back over the edge of the bed so that he could help Mother. When she was back on her feet, she too laughed at the bed's wilful behaviour. Father fetched his tools. He had to replace a broken bracket. I heard him tapping, cursing now and then, then laughing. In between he talked about a similar misfortune that had befallen his parents. I only heard isolated words. All the same, I got the gist of the story.

Grandfather must have been president of the Zermatt *burgers* – an association of the oldest families – at that time. There was a reception with free wine. Grandfather not only took his wife to it, but his fiddle, on which he could play cheerful dance tunes. It must have been an unusually merry evening, as both of them could hardly stand when they got home.

Grandfather and Grandmother spared themselves the trouble of taking off their clothes and shoes and threw themselves down on the bed as they were. The children were afraid Grandfather might fall out of bed in the night, as Grandmother left him too little room. They took a long strap from some old mule harness and strapped their parents down.

When Grandfather wanted to get up in the night, he could not free himself from his wife.

"Dammit", he yelled, "Now I'm really stuck up with my old lady!"

My father took special delight in this story. My mother laughed too. Now they were back in bed talking. Just as I was dropping off to sleep, I heard my name mentioned, and at once I was wide awake. Mother seemed to be worried about something. I gradually understood what it was about. In his acquisitive enthusiasm at the inn Father had bought the Kalbermatte pasture as well. We were now obliged to keep livestock on it for the next four years. But we had only two cows, a calf, two goats and, depending on the time of year, three or four sheep or two pigs. Oh yes, I almost forgot the chickens. But they had no place on the pasture.

If I had understood properly, Father planned to hire a maid to make cheese. He wanted to send me with her and all the animals up to the pasture. This is what worried Mother. She thought an eight-year-old boy too young for such work. "He's still a child. How can you expect the poor boy to manage?"

Ears pricked, I listened to my parents. "Think of all the dangers during the long summer: rain, landslides, floods, overhanging grass. And what if it should snow?"

I thought Mother too apprehensive. It wasn't half as bad as she said.

"Is there a kitchen in the hut?"

"There's a fireplace," my father replied.

"And a corner where they can have their meals?"

"They can eat in front of the hut. There's a little wall to sit on along the front. And a stone table."

"And if it rains?"

"If it rains! Then they sit on the edge of the bed with their plates on their laps. I've told you it isn't a Grand Hotel."

There was a long silence. Mother thought it advisable to leave a pause. I should have liked to chime in: "Yes, Mother, I like eating out of doors at a stone table, better than in a Grand Hotel." Though I had never, of course, eaten in a Grand Hotel.

"But then there's this stupid business..." Mother picked up the conversation. "That idiotic story! – You know what I mean."

"What story?"ˋ

"About..." She said it so quietly I could not catch the next words.

"Silly gossip!"

"Don't forget the boy was born in the third week of December. They especially like appearing to people born then."

I caught my breath. That was how people talked about ghosts. And so it was. Someone who could not find eternal rest had to do penance in the hut. Now that was a different kettle of fish. To live in a place where you can eat out of doors at a stone table is just a good adventure, but to sleep in a hut where dead people come and go – that's not pleasant. I shuddered at the thought of waking up at night to find a ghost standing by my bed. Perhaps an old man with a disfigured face, with straggly hair and beard and the fixed, lifeless stare of the Beyond. Your heart stops, your breath won't come, your arms are paralysed. And your legs! You can't take a single step. And your voice won't work. You are frozen into a mummy. And the ghost comes closer and closer, slowly, without moving a muscle of its face. Who hasn't had dreams like this? What a relief to wake up. But to have a meeting like that when wide awake, in full consciousness – that's no trivial matter.

Mother resumed the conversation: "But Biner Anton's already met him!"

"Nonsense," said Father impatiently. "He didn't meet him. He only heard him. That's different."

Mother still wasn't satisfied: "He's supposed to have been tending sheep in Momat when he heard that frightful wailing from the Kalbermatte across the valley."

"Maybe. What's so terrible about that? There has to be justice. When he was alive, that fellow had lured other people's sheep into his trap to shear them. That was wooltheft. It has to be atoned for."

"Anton hardly had time to rush back to the hut and bolt the door. He said the howling from outside the hut was terrible! He shouted over and over again: 'Woe, woe, woe, eternities of woe'".

Father mumbled something about divine justice. The conversation died down for a time. "Anyway, I'll put a good bolt on the door," Father yawned.

"Let's hope that will be enough to protect our poor boy! Children born in that week don't have an easy life as far as such things are concerned." I stared up at the ceiling. The streetlamp was still rocking the light across it. By turns I saw the knots in the boards or gazed into the velvet shadows of the night. This game brought the knots to life. They turned into insistently staring eyes; dozens of eyes were fixed on me, then vanished again. I grew afraid. "I don't want to go up to the pasture. Never. I'd rather run wild". "Running wild" meant running away from home. If possible with half a loaf under your arm, so that you could hide in a hut or under an overhanging rock. And never, never come back to my parents. I had tried it more than once. But each time, at the end of the day, the evening had come with dusk, darkness and fear. And I was happy to run back home, put up with the mockery of my parents and brothers and sisters and again be part of a family whose advantages outweighed those of running wild.

Chain

Refuse pits had a special fascination for us children. They were full of surprises. The hotel guests were very generous when it came to throwing things away. I once found a box of caramel toffees buried under rotting vegetable peelings and tin cans. You could dig out and open a hundred boxes and they would all be empty. But this box still had all its eight toffees. They were packed individually in tissue paper. True, the box had suffered somewhat. It had been too long in the rubbish and had not withstood the rain and dirt with complete impunity. All the same, I was beside myself with joy at my find, stuffed it into my pocket and left the rubbish heap. In the village square I met Anni and I shared my booty with her, fully aware that I had earned her lifelong gratitude.

Anni was my friend at school. According to the scribbling in new snow and on a number of walls, we were already engaged. "Anni's got Hannes", you could read, and "Hannes is Anni's Sweetheart". Such inscriptions were very annoying to a boy. Because they were anonymous, no-one could be walloped for them. Either you bore them with dignity, or you took a large piece of chalk and avenged yourself on the likeliest suspect in even bigger letters.

Admittedly, I felt attracted from an early age to the tender sex. This weakness has never left me. Even now I still prefer a ladies' coffee-party to any discussion with important gentlemen. Having to listen to talk about how someone was told where to get off, or tedious accounts of troop movements during military service, are the worst things that can happen to me. I prefer to hear about the problems of some little bed-wetter, or how a neighbour has cut her roses, or the latest about Frau Meier, who is reputed to have been sighted with her family doctor in Mallorca. I have often wondered why I should value female company more. Perhaps because I was already in such close contact to a girl in my mother's womb, even before I came into the world. I am a twin. Of my little sister I know only her grave with the thistles and the white cross, so soon did she give her life back to her Maker. I hope I'm not partly to blame. Is it possible that I claimed too much of the warmth below Mother's heart and that the tiny girl could not defend herself? We know what boys can be like!

Anni wore a big, light-blue bow in her hair, which hung down loosely over her shoulders. She had white socks on and summer shoes. Her pretty light dress of printed sateen blew out in the wind. It didn't bother her that I trotted beside her in heavy nailed shoes and patched, calf-length trousers. My shirt had a bad tear in it again, and my hair had been cut about a millimetre long by my father, with just a little tuft in front. When we reached a deserted alley, I kissed her timidly on the cheek. Delighted, she gave me her hand and ran with me and our young love through the darkening village. Another time I found in the garden of the Hotel Gornergrat a fragment of red glass that must have come from a broken veranda window. It was confusing to look at the world through the glass. The stream whirled through red gullies like congealing blood. Clouds and snowy peaks lay in an eternal alpine sunset. The world looked like a lost paradise.

For one summer I kept the piece of glass in my coat pocket. There was no flower, beetle or insect, no sunset or thunderstorm that was not magically transformed by the glass.

But then somehow it found its way into Anni's toy box. Perhaps I would have given it to her earlier, but it was around this time that Anni's mother began calling every time I ventured near her door: "Come on, Anni! Here's your boy-friend!" This was too embarrassing. One of my schoolmates could easily have heard it...

Once again my trousers were showing their true age via an epidemic of patches. More than once my mother had drawn my father's attention to the state of the garment. "The boy really must have a new pair of trousers when he goes back to school." Father knew how to joke his way out of such obligations for as long as possible. This time he avoided the expense altogether. Quite unexpectedly I was given a fine navy-blue outfit by Anni's mother; her youngest son had grown out of it. It fitted me as if it had been made to measure. And it was smart, distinguished – but not very hard-wearing.

As luck would have it, the youngsters of the "upper village" decided to play "chain" on that Sunday.

I threw myself vigorously into the game, wearing my navy-blue suit. Having once started, holes in your clothing simply didn't count. Leaps from stable and summerhouse roofs on to manure heaps and into gardens were all part of the game. Crawling along furrows in muddy fields was unavoidable. And periodic hiding in dirty stables or dusty sheds was essential if you did not want to spoil your chances of winning.

In the whole world there is no more exciting game for unruly boys than chain. It takes hold of you like a drunken frenzy. It's not an ordinary game, but reality turned into play. The players divide into two sides, police and convicts. In a square in the upper village, from which streets and alleys led out on all sides, a corner of a house was designated the prison. The police counted to a hundred. With this start the convicts made their getaway. Now the agents of the law tried to hunt down the convicts in their hideouts and run them in. If a policeman managed to touch a convict with his hand, the convict had to go to "prison". The first prisoner held on to the corner of the house with one hand. He held out his other hand to the next prisoner. This produced a chain that got longer and longer as more convicts joined the chain. The convicts still at liberty could free their comrades who had been caught. By touching one of them and shouting "Free!" you could make them all free men again. The chain was therefore guarded by police. The guards had to make sure no liberator could get to the chain from the many narrow streets. But the chain could move like a snake. It impeded the guards in their task. It could unwind now into this alley, now into that like a dragon's tail. It would fake a danger signal, then suddenly dart into a different lane, where a liberator leapt out of hiding, reached the prisoners and freed them with a slap of the hand. "Free!" shouted all the boisterous lads together. Off they ran, while the guards tried to collar as many as possible all over again.: "Got you! And you!" And so it went on. A new chain formed, and the game continued. It never lost its thrill. No other game had anything like the same fascination for me. I became totally intoxicated with my role as liberator or policeman.

On this memorable Sunday a very long chain had formed. Only a few convicts were still free. It looked as if the police had won the game.

In my navy-blue gabardine suit I was crouching on the roof of a stable near the chain. When I raised my head over the gutter, I could see the chain and the many guards in the street below. I crept as near to the edge of the roof as I could and waited for a propitious moment. The chain had to come snaking in the direction of the dung-heap next to the stable. The warm autumn days seemed to have given the dung-heap a good supportive crust.

The chain suddenly snaked past the heap. With heroic zeal I jumped up and threw myself from the roof on to the dubious surface. It spurted like a fountain. With both legs I was knee-deep in manure. With one hand I touched a prisoner and shouted "Free!" at the top of my voice. But then the laughter started, and almost brought the game to a stop. I was hunting in the mire for my left shoe, as I had pulled out my foot without it. Some of the prisoners laughed so much the police had no trouble re-arresting them. I retreated shamefaced to the village well, which soon turned into a coffee-coloured sewer. With my suit wringing wet I made for home, where the predictable sequel awaited me.

Under the sign of Taurus

We had hardly time to finish our gruel. Mother gave Father a meaningful look and we were sent early to bed. I shared a pull-out bed with Rudolf. During the day it was pushed, foot-end first, under our sister's bed. We called it our "drawer bed".

That evening another bed had suddenly appeared in the kitchen, in the corner where up to then a bowl for our daily face-washing had stood on a rickety wooden stand. I heard Father run along the arbour and tramp down the staircase.

"What's going on?" I asked my sister.

"You'll find out soon enough," came the answer.

"Are we getting a visitor?"

"Of course, otherwise they wouldn't have put the bed out."

There was nothing more to be got out of her.

Hardly were we in our beds when Father's footsteps were heard on the staircase again. He had a neighbouring woman with him. They went together into the kitchen. Mother seemed to be expecting them.

"A good thing you've come so quickly, Marie. We've no time to lose," I heard Mother say.

Saucepan lids began to clatter on the stove. Father had to go several times to the store-room. There were some things he could not find. Mother called out to him where to look. "Maybe I would find them," I thought.

Those were no ordinary goings-on in the kitchen. Prick my ears as I might, I couldn't make out what was happening. It all seemed to revolve around Mother. Now and then I thought I heard stifled sounds that were new to me. But then Mother's voice could be heard again. There was nothing untoward about it. All the same, there was a tension in the house. More than once I wondered if I should go and have a look. But something held me back. Perhaps it was my sister, who commanded from time to time: "Get to sleep, will you!"

Suddenly I heard what seemed to be the cries of a child. No question, they came from the kitchen. I jumped out of bed. But my sister caught me before I reached the door and sent me back to bed.

"Can't you hear? That's a child crying!" I said reproachfully.

"So? Mother's had a baby."

"Had a baby? Don't talk such nonsense! She would have told me. Did we say we wanted a baby?"

She just laughed. Rudolf too was still awake: "A baby? A baby sister?"

"How should I know? Mother will show it to you in the morning. But you're not allowed in the kitchen now."

I doubted what my sister was saying. Sisters always thought they knew more than we did. I couldn't believe it. "Had a baby? So suddenly?" I was by no means pleased. Little brothers and sisters always meant a lot of work, particularly for their elder brothers and sisters. Hardly can the little creature lie on its stomach when you're asked to look after it. Every fly that tickles its nose is your fault. And when it gets to its feet and pulls everything down, you have to answer for it. Your schoolmates are playing wild games in front of your house, and you have to tramp along behind the new acquisition, making sure it doesn't hit its head on something. And watch out if anything does happen. Then you find out that big brother's ears are not treated with the same respect as the little one's.

Aunt Magdalena had once said: "The storks are far too eager in these parts!"

It was a silly thing to say. I'd known for a long time where babies came from. Older school-friends had explained it to me. In a manner that farm boys could readily understand: "Father's the bull – Mother's the cow. Of course they don't do it in a field, but at home in their bed. Andreas Bächer and Severin Thamatter do it with their wives three times a day! Yes, really. My God, you live behind the times. Ask your sister."

This explanation had set my mind in a turmoil. What? My parents doing something like that? Impossible! I could perhaps imagine my father doing it. But my mother? No. That was not like her at all!

How often had I taken cows to be mated. My goodness, the way they behaved! You had all sorts of trouble even before they got to the bull. Once a cow climbed with its forelegs on to my shoulders and pushed me over, it was so confused. It wanted to ride me.

And then the bull! It bunched up its lips, rolled its eyes and could hardly be held. I was sorry for the young cows. They were afraid. You had to hold them and pull their tails to one side so that the bull could mount them. When the bull took the scent, opened his nostrils and snorted, before rearing up and seeking the cow with his long rod, the people looking on got very excited. I always found the bull's strong movements and the wild act of procreation obscurely alarming.

My mother really couldn't do anything like that. She, who was respected by everyone. She was always helpful. When an unmarried girl brought a child into the world but could produce no milk to feed it, the pious women from the upper village nodded knowingly when they met her in the street. Their dark looks made it clear that they were on God's side and entirely endorsed His withholding the milk. Mother had given birth to my younger brother at the same time. She had milk in abundance. She went to see the unmarried girl and offered to suckle her child. And she was supposed to do something so foolish? I had to talk to her.

She was busy washing up. I put it to her straight. No beating about the bush with me! She listened calmly. When I had got my disillusionment off my chest, she said: "How can your friend tell you such a thing? You can't compare people with animals. Or do your friends eat from a trough like piglets? People love each other. Believe me, that's quite different. You'll find that out later when it happens to you."

"I will never let this happen to me. Never! Not something like that."

After this conversation there was a peculiar tension between my mother and me for a time. I was often very short with her. She showed a lot of patience, but treated me more coolly than I was used to.

I remembered all this while the baby made occasional noises in the kitchen. Footsteps and saucepan lids could still be heard, but the talk seemed to be growing calmer. It wasn't worth pricking up my ears any more. I fell asleep.

When I awoke next morning, curiosity drove me into the kitchen with my nightshirt on. Mother was lying in bed and greeted me with a smile. Before her stood a cradle. I looked cautiously behind the check curtain. A downy little head was to be seen, with wrinkles all over its forehead. The snub nose and the open, searching mouth looked pretty. "You've got a little brother," said Mother. "Are you pleased?"

I looked at the pink little creature and nodded suspiciously: "But he's already covered with in wrinkles."

My sister had to do the housework. Mother gave her instructions from her bed. After three days she was back at the stove as usual. Life went back to its familiar routine. With some new tasks and more work for Mother.

Spring market

The long winter was weighing on us. Our spirits finally rose when at last we heard the water dripping from the roofs and the Foehn sighing in the woods. The weight of the snow had bent the smaller trees and the bushes. The ground looked as if it had been flattened by a steamroller. Yet already, flowers were sprouting from the earth everywhere.

All it took was a small area of snow-free ground, a few rays of sun, and the glowing orange coltsfoot awoke. It was the first messenger of spring in a landscape still gripped by snow. The little fringed bell of the soldanella trembled timorously in the wind. Often its violet head could be seen poking through a thin crust of snow. Then white and blue crocusses would cover an entire hollow, shining dully against the light while the first bees visited them. On the forest floor liverwort bloomed, and in rock crevices the pinkish-mauve hearts of the mountain primrose. Finally, the dandelion gilded the whole valley with its strong yellow. Spring was here. And anyone who did not believe it could hear it from the cuckoo calling from every wood.

The animals grew restless. When they were led from their stables to be watered, they frisked about, kicked up their hind legs and could hardly be held by their halters. But the people too felt the spring. Father stood long at the window. As every year, he felt the urge to go to the cattle market at Sion. A piglet had to be bought. Of course, it could have been ordered from a good sty. It was to be had for a fraction of the cost of the trip, for Father never finished with the market in a day. But what sort of a pig is it that's sent to you unseen!

"I'd rather not have one," he declared. "I want an animal with a curly tail. And it must curl clockwise. They turn out well."

Father was not the only one to travel to the Sion market. From all the valleys of Valais they came, his old friends. They shook hands, drank frequently to each other's health, slapped each other on the shoulder, teased each other, laughed and gossiped. Men, too, could babble away when they met over a good glass of Fendant.

Once they were of such good cheer that they missed the market altogether. When they wanted to start buying, they noticed the clock had skipped a full day. The municipal workers were busy clearing the market-place. Not an animal in sight. Reason enough to drown the surprise at the nearest bar, taking it with a sense of humour. But reason, too, to go back home rather out of sorts, complaining there had been nothing worth buying. Naturally, we were disappointed when Father arrived at the station with no animals, just his rope and rucksack, to be accompanied glumly home while everyone else gloated over their purchases.

Normally, Father was successful. He found the piglet he was looking for with the clockwise curl in its tail and was already good friends with it when he got home. He praised his good bargain. Under fifteen francs. He didn't mention the travel costs, at least four times as much. Mother knew about them, but held her peace. Father thought: Man does not live by bread alone when he goes to market. He had also found a maid who was to help me tend our mountain pasture. The postmaster had telephoned the priest of Törbel to ask him to send a suitable girl.

The day the maid arrived, Father was freshly shaven. He wore his moustache with a raffish twist at the tips. As head of the family he wanted to make a dignified impression on her. He always had a special gleam in his eye when there were women about.

Father fetched Karolina from the station and carried her wicker basket with her few possessions to our house. He was in good heart, joking with the young shepherdess. We spent the whole evening sitting together. In the soft light of the kitchen lamp Father told of his adventures among the wild Kurds in the Caucasus. We sang our songs about the Little Billy Goat and the Polish Maid. We all felt the summer separation ahead of us. Father had to take up his post in the Alpine Museum in Zermatt. As we had let the apartment to visitors, he lived in a little room above the chicken coop. Mother had taken her job as cook at the Matterhorn cabin again. Lina worked at the tearoom in Zumsee and looked after her two little brothers.

It was a simple wooden building with an area in front of it for guests who wanted to sit down to enjoy a glass of milk or a cup of tea in the sun. Mother put pots of flowers outside the windows of our house and on the low walls of the teagarden. Fennel, geraniums and marguerites vied with the Swiss flag fluttering on the roof to offer guests a friendly greeting. And anyone who was still undecided whether to stop could consult the big wooden notice with its painted frame for his secret wish. "Teehüttli Aroleid. Fresh Alpine milk, Coffee, Tea, Hot Chocolate, Lemonade, Mineral Water. Refreshments." All that was to be had cheaply from us.

And I had to go up to the alp with Karolina. Mother was sorry to see our family torn apart for eight or ten weeks, each of us having to earn our living in a different place. She thought it could have been arranged differently, but Father decided how the money for the long winter was to be scraped together.

The biblical Noah, who had an eye for animals and had seen many strange sights on his voyage in the Ark, would have feasted his eyes had he peered cautiously over the edge of a cloud to see our exodus up the mountain. He would have seen a motley group making its way through the Arufluh larch woods to reach the Kalbermatte via Zmutt and Bodmen.

According to Father's instructions I led the way. In a basket covered with a cloth I carried on my back four hens clucking in protest when I ran to drive a cow or goat out of a clover meadow, unceremoniously shaking the basket. At the same time I led our old nanny-goat Hasa on a rope. In keeping with her age she displayed a certain good sense and obedience. We expected her to set a good example to the other animals as she bleated on ahead. All winter she had been tied up beside the lead cow. The two animals got on well. So Tschäggi the cow followed willingly behind her little friend. Behind them came the rest of the goats and cattle.

Karolina carried the copper vessel for cheese-making, the milking stool, the milking equipment and her personal effects in a big basket on her back. She drove the cows and goats forward if they lingered too long over the fresh grass. Goats are compulsive nibblers. Nothing is safe from their inventive gluttony. She had more trouble with these wilful, horned ladies than with the placid cows. I could hear from the sound of the large and small bells whether the procession was making leisurely progress, was pausing for a snack or going totally out of control.

Behind Karolina came the sheep. Sheep are herd animals. They are unimaginative, blind followers. The mere appearance of a dog can be enough to cause havoc, filling them with panic fear. Then they can plunge witlessly over a cliff. Mother therefore kept them under her eye. She followed them with swaying hips, a basket full of kitchen utensils and food on her back.

Father had saved the hardest task for himself. He drove the two little pigs before him on the end of a rope. He and the two young animals were liable to disagree over the best route to follow. Anticipating this, he had tied a rope to a back leg of each animal. He held the two ends in one hand. In the other he wielded a birch rod, with which he settled any differences over direction, pace or whether to take a rest. Usually, I admit, such deliberations were accompanied by squeaks of protest from his pupils. In his basket Father carried tools and materials. In one of the two sheds he wanted to install a fireplace with a chimney to be used for cheesemaking.

In Grisette a landslide had swept the path down for a stone throw's distance. We had to feign especial calm to get the animals across the moraine slope without undue alarm. Both we and the animals were tired when we finally reached the pasture. We set down our baskets and rested on the grass.

Karolina chewed a stem of grass which had heart-shaped, purple flowers at the end. We called it tremble-grass. She looked at me with moss-green eyes that shone between dark lashes. There was a curious smile on her full lips as she said:

"Well, what a good boy you've been."

A roof over our heads

Father was in excellent spirits. He felt at home in the high pasture. Every rock he came across was a delight to him: he knew all their names given to them by earlier shepherds. Once baptised, the rocky crags and erratic boulders kept their names.

My parents had already been up once to the Kalbermatte. Father had built the brick fireplace for the cheese copper, and Mother had prepared the straw sacks for the two beds. Now the places to lie had to be provided with the necessary bedclothes and the cheese-making equipment installed. Father and I attached the pivoted arm to the wall, so that the big copper vat could be hung over the fire. We fixed hanging shelves to the ceiling beams. Father could already see them laden with full-fat alpine cheese. The mice could not reach these hanging shelves. That was important, as the old lofts were the perfect breeding ground for rodents. Karolina scrubbed the hut and the cheese dairy clean and helped Mother. The animals ate the lush grass greedily.

The two sheds and the little hut huddled against the rock wall for protection against the winter landslides. In front of the hut lay the large crescent-shaped meadow. Along the far side there was a steep drop to the Zmuttbach, whose roar was heard constantly. A rickety stone wall enclosed the level pasture.

"Grandfather and I built this wall when I was young," Father told us. "I looked after our sheep here. Your great-grandfather built the second stable as well." Father was in the best of spirits.

"And the hut. Did he build that too?" Mother asked rather pointedly.

Father was annoyed by the tacit reproach.

"I don't know about that," he returned. "But it can't be altered now. I've already told you it's not a luxury villa."

He considered the hut a perfectly habitable billet for a summer on the alp. There was a glitter in Mother's eye, but she said nothing. Father turned to me.

"I'll show you how to light the juniper bushes to turn them into firewood. Only burn as many as you need for the two hearths. Juniper must be able to renew itself."

We lit some bushes. The needles burned like tinder. Of the green wood, only the bark and the tips of the twigs were charred. "When the branches are left bare in the sun, they soon dry out. You can easily break them from the root. They burn well, as you'll see. And the roots will put out new shoots." Father made me aware of the dangers the animals were exposed to. Then he put me in charge of the pasture with the gesture of someone abdicating the Promised Land. He left behind some of his tools and a number of nails, patted me kindly on the shoulder, became noticeably more subdued and said to Mother:

"Come, Barbara. Let's go."

Mother had a lot that she might have said, though she had said a good deal already. It was hard for her to leave me and the animals to an uncertain fate. She did not think it would turn out well, I could feel that. She took me in her arms and said quietly:

"Don't forget to pray, my son, and look after yourself."

She followed my father down to the valley.

The little hut, which had been built years before as a shelter for shepherds, everywhere showed signs of not having been lived in for decades. The simple iron stove threatened to fall apart. A crack as wide as a finger split the rusty contraption in two. I found a piece of rusty wire on the fence enclosing the meadow. It was very fragile, but I succeeded in tying it round the stove and knotting the ends.

Everything was rusty, even the nails Karolina wanted to hang the clothes from. I hammered them into the wall with the axe and knocked in new nails where Karolina wanted them. More was not to be done on the first day.

The cattle and goats had to be driven into the shed and tied up. It was some time before every animal was satisfied with the place allotted to it and was able to be milked. The pigs grunted in their enclosure in a corner of the shed, begging for the food Mother had put out ready for them. The sheep spent the night under an overhanging rock above the hut. The four hens that were to supply us with eggs for our own consumption were locked in the barn. They had to get used to their new accommodation. By sunset they were already on their perches, waiting for night. We all had a roof over our heads.

Karolina and I drank fresh milk and ate bread and cheese. When I wanted to lock the little door leading into the kitchen, I noticed that it had no lock. And the door leading from the kitchen to the outside was just resting against its frame. That was not reassuring. The nearest human habitation was an hour's march down the valley. Our hut lay on the path over the pass to Zinal. Mountaineers without guides often walked into the mountains at night and slept in a barn or a deserted hut. Then there was this restless soul, the wool thief of Kalbermatte, who had sheared other people's sheep and had to atone for his misdeeds. You didn't want to find him standing beside your bed when you woke in the night. So the door needed a good solid lock. I managed to bar it for the first night with a thick branch.

Kitchen is too grand a word for the little room it referred to. When Karolina stood at the stove, it was not possible to enter the bedroom unless she squeezed into the corner. The door took up the whole room. There was no space for a table, stool or chest. But there weren't any such things. The little stove stood on a low wall. Beside it there was room for the water bucket and a little firewood. On a sooty shelf above the stove Karolina placed the many old, square biscuit boxes that Mother had brought for us to keep food in. In them flour, maize, pasta, sugar and salt were safe from the mice. In the loose, unplastered masonry lived field-mice with silky fur, cunning round eyes and pointed, bright-pink ears. Our presence just made them curious. They hardly minded us, darting along the stone wall and watching what we were doing.

The bedroom was hardly bigger. Karolina's bed took up the whole width of the room, head against one wall, foot against the other. The builder had screwed the sides of the bed to the wall beams with little wooden blocks, so that a separate frame was not needed. The room had three windows, above the pillow, at the foot end and in the middle. One of the four panes could be slid open from inside or outside. That was unpleasant, as the windows were at chest height.

"Tomorrow you'll have to nail shut the sliding windows above my head and in the middle," Karolina commanded. "I don't want anyone opening the windows in the night and pulling my hair or tickling my tummy."

She like to make little jokes like that. She had a sense of humour, which was needed in such a place. Only cheerful people could survive the loneliness of an Alpine summer unscathed.

Lying on my straw sack, I turned over in my mind what still needed to be patched up and done. A simple WC had to be built in the corner between the shed and the hut. There were plenty of stones lying around. Some kind soul had left a few old boards in the barn. On the roofs the weight of the snow had moved the stone slabs. They needed to be pushed back into position. You could see clearly the places where the rain had dripped through. The biggest job was clearing out the ditch that took the drinking water to the meadow. The channel was overgrown and blocked in places, and the water from the Titerbach could not get through.

While I considered how the front door could be properly locked, the wind rattled the window panes. The rushing sound of the wild Zmuttbach rose to a sigh, then was interrupted by a cow-bell and the sound of tugging on a chain. Karolina was lying on her back. I thought she wasn't asleep but looking at the ceiling. Perhaps she had imagined life on the mountain somewhat differently. A star twinkled through the dirty window pane.

I tried not to think about the ghost known far and wide as the "Kalbermattubotzu" – the Spook of Kalbermatte. No-one knew exactly where it lived. But it was always heard near the hut. Its fearsome bleating, as if a dozen sheep were being torn to pieces, must have been terrible to hear. I just hoped the dead man had at last worked off his guilt for the stolen wool and found eternal peace. I once thought I heard noises that sounded like sheep, but told myself they must come from our flock. Luckily I was very tired and fell asleep before the unquiet soul could set my thoughts racing.

Next morning Karolina was up early. She lit a wood fire in the stove to boil a cup of milk. The smoke could not escape through the flue. It gradually filled the kitchen. Coughing and cursing with streaming eyes, she came into the main room. It turned out that snow or a rock fall had bent and squashed the part of the flue projecting above the roof. I took off the flue, pulled it over a round beam and hammered it back roughly into its original shape.

It was very difficult to find suitable wood for repairs. Our side of the valley was unwooded. There were just two or three crooked little trees growing out of crevices in the rock. On the shaded side of the valley a sparse wood stretched over the Stafelalp to Momat. On that side there was wood in plenty. The rushing stream, without a bridge in the neighbourhood, blocked our access to it. Luckily the wall had been mended with boards in places. I removed the boards and shaped them with the axe. To block the windows I split some small pegs and nailed them to the frame. The two panes could not be slid, either from inside or from outside". If I'd known you didn't even have a dog,

I should have taken Uncle Caesar's Bari with me," said Karolina. "He would have lain on the bed at my feet and got his teeth into anyone who reached through the window."

I thought: It would be nice to have a dog; but I replied: "Who do you expect to come walking past here at night?"

"Oh, just wait till the mountaineering gets going."

"Even if someone does walk past, he's not going to creep round the house to grab you through the window!"

"Who knows? Perhaps a handsome young mountain guide! I know what men are like."

She laughed and stretched her bosom till the top two buttons of her bodice burst open.

My bed was only half as high as Karolina's. It lay half under her bed at right-angles to it. It took up the whole length of the room. My head was next to the door and my feet under her bedstead. On the other side of the door a wider bed was fixed, a guest's bed. But we neither expected not wanted guests. The frame served as a seat. In bad weather we sat with our plates on our knees, wordlessly eating our boiled maize soaked in creamy milk.

In the heap of stones to the west of the hut Karolina had discovered a weasel as she was going over to the cow-shed in the morning. She was very worried, claiming that weasels liked to bite cattle in the legs and suck their blood. This made the cattle lame for a time. I had never heard of this and calmed her down by saying: "Don't worry, I'll chase it away. When the wind comes from the valley, I'll burn some old rags. The wind will blow the stinking fumes into the scree and smoke out the hiding holes. Weasels can't stand that."

Karolina gave me a strange look from the corner of her eyes:

"I can't imagine where you've got all that from."

"What have I got?"

"Oh, nothing," she said with a smile.

At the world's end

Not far from the moraine of the Zmutt glacier there was a hollow where the cattle were especially fond of grazing. I lay on a little knoll, resting my chin on my hands, chewing a straw and watching the animals. I liked to hear them greedily tearing the grass, shaking their bells and snorting noisily.

The sun warmed my back and made me sleepy. I was not allowed to fall asleep, for behind the hill I was lying on was a steep slope down to the Zmuttbach. A bleak morainic slope, on which no vegetation could take root. Constant erosion had made it look like a silver-grey cliff. Only a couple of edelweiss bushes were trying to get a foothold.

The turf at the edge of the cliff was hollowed out underneath. For some metres it was completely unsupported. A danger for the cattle if they ventured too close. That is why I was lying in the grass, fighting against sleep.

More than once I had resolved to cut away the overhanging turf with a pick, but I regularly forgot to take the implement with me when I drove the animals up to the moraine.

The goats were picking at the slope leading up to the rocks. Goats do not feed greedily. They take a leaf here, a bloom or bud there, if it has been foolish enough to open itself to the world just when a little bearded goat is tripping past. Goats are like cats. They don't obey willingly, doing so only when they sense an advantage to themselves, or when they have no choice. They are horned individualists. They are used to danger and have a clear understanding of their own climbing skills. It can happen that young, inexperienced kids get stranded in the rocks and bleat for help. Then they don't mind being picked up and carried out of danger.

I turned on my back and looked up at the dry cloud shapes the west wind was driving across the blue sky from the direction of the Gabelhorn and the Zinalrothorn. Dazzling clouds that took the shape of grimacing faces, figures, dragons. Often, Moses looked down with his flowing beard. The Madonna pulled off one of the Child's arms. The Winged Dragon disintegrated in the wind and re-formed as a question mark. Sheep hurried after one another only to fall victim, like all the rest of the prolific jumble, to the warm rays of the sun.

My sheep were grazing high above on the rocky ledges. At midday I could not see them. They had sought the shade of an overhanging rock. In the morning and evening they grazed on one of the steep slopes. Now and then I would visit them, give them salt from the palm of my hand and exchange a few words with them. They were healthy and well fleeced.

A group of tourists with guides and bearers was sweating up the stony path towards the Schönbühl cabin. It was high summer and there had been a long dry period. The world belonged to the crickets. Where the path was moistened by ground-water there were swarms of blue butterflies. A beetle was lying on its back in the grass. It tried to get back on its feet with jerks of the head. At each attempt you could hear a soft ticking. On my palm it was able to project itself a few inches into the air in this mysterious way, hoping to land on its feet. It was a peaceful afternoon. Not even the joyous cries of the fair Helena were to be heard from the Stafelalp. Perhaps she was sleeping with her desires in the shade of a pine.

You could hear the wingbeat of the tortoiseshell butterfly. The bright humming of gnats and flies. The soft buzz of wasps and the deep drone of bumble-bees. All these different chords mingled with the soft splashing of a nearby spring. My eyes began to close. No – I was not to sleep. From the Tiefmatt glacier below the Matterhorn's north face a fall of ice thundered down on to the Zmutt glacier. An avalanche. Then it was still again. The sigh of the Arvenbach waterfall was borne to me in snatches on the wind. A delicate mist lay across the valley. It was the blue midday.

I had grown used to solitude. Days and weeks of being alone. A whole summer. A life at the end of the world. Without a pocket knife. Without a clock. Without toys. I tried to imitate the sounds of the wind. To murmur like springs. To frighten the marmots with their own warning cry. To hold conversations with the mountains. Sometimes I seemed to understand the language of animals. And I heard words no-one had spoken. Perhaps they were water dripping in a secluded cave. Or stray sounds from far off falling into the stillness.

No books. I read the big eyes of the cattle. I saw when they were sad. Sad for no reason, it seemed to me. They lacked nothing. Yet sometimes they looked at the world as if their souls had been torn from their bodies.

I scratched them between the horns and behind the ears. Stroked their long chins with my palm. They lifted their heads and shut their eyes. I pressed my head against their necks.

They accepted the tenderness. Water flowed from their eyes. For me it was tears. Who knows what goes on inside an animal?

On other days they were exuberant, tossed their tails and hind legs, challenged me to race them, were quarrelsome and stubborn. Then they had to deal with a cowherd who knew how to wield a branch or anything else that came to hand, who showed them who was master. In such cases there was no room for arguments.

The son of the warden of the Schönbühl cabin came past us along the track. Every day he fetched a rucksack stuffed with food and drink from Zermatt. He was my age. But he wore a beret and spoke French. On rainy days I often put a jute sack inside out on my head. I talked the Valais dialect. We couldn't understand each other. He just went: "Brrrr!" I nodded to him and watched him go on his way. He had to lean far forward to keep his balance. His stick with its hooked handle hung round his neck.

The west wind sent clouds from the Hohlicht sailing into the empty sky. Their shadows fell across the rocks on the valley floor. Like flying nets they crossed the Zmuttbach and fled through the branches of the pinewood up to the crests of the hills. Leaving the world behind. Sometimes the sun burned as if a thunderstorm were brewing. My eyelids closed.

Two or three times, between the blooming arnica, bearberry and juniper, I caught sight of the herd with its monotonous chiming. The cow-bells spread an illusion of security. The wind gusted across the pasture. I felt its fingers in my unruly hair. It was good to feel the wind. It fidgeted with my shirt. Felt my bare chest. Then tore my shirt from my body. Played with it. Went flapping off with it. I tried to catch it. It danced away from my clumsy fingers. Someone called my name. A large spider crawled over a stone. I stumbled and fell over a cliff. I fell and fell into emptiness. Again someone called my name. My face was wiped with a wet cloth. I started in fear. Tschäggi, the lead-cow, was licking my face with her rough tongue. I must have fallen asleep.

The cow was always trying to lick my forehead. Less out of affection than because of the salty residue of sweat that gathered there. I had long given up washing in the ice-cold well. In any case, we had no mirror. We only saw other people's faces. And very few of them.

The cattle were grazing close to the overhanging turf. I jumped up and drove them carefully back into the hollow. How easily one of them might have stepped on to the undermined margin! I looked down the steep slope to the water. How careless I had been! And again someone called my name. This time I heard it distinctly coming from the valley.

Karolina in her nailed shoes was striding towards me up the path from the hut. When she noticed I had seen her, she waved her arm. She pointed down towards the stable.

Something's wrong with the pigs. Or a hawk has taken a hen. Perhaps I've left the stable door open and the pigs have got out.

"Coming," I called as loud as I could. Quickly I drove the herd to a slope where I could leave them unattended for a while.

Strobel

I hurried across the stony slope to the hut.

"One of the pigs is ill," Karolina called from a distance. "It doesn't eat and it's lying down like a dead thing."

I looked as if the end of the world was near.

"It was still all right this morning," I replied.

"I took them their swill. Only one came to the trough. That made me suspicious. What's up with the other, I wondered. I look over the barrier, and what do I see? It's lying on the ground with its legs sticking out. Jesus, I said, that pig's ill."

It was dark in the shed. I was still dazzled by the sun. I couldn't see anything and had to wait.

"Can't you see them yet? The smaller one's lying on the floor," said Karolina impatiently.

"The one with the white spot on his nose?"

"Yes."

"That's Strobel." I'd given him that name.

I climbed over the barrier. The bigger animal came up to me grunting and rubbed its snout against my trousers. The other one lay on the ground. I knelt beside him.

"What's the matter, Strobel? Don't give us any trouble, please." When I said his name, he opened his eyes and tried to grunt without lifting his head. "Are you feeling as bad as that?" I put my hand between his ears.

"Goodness, the animal's got a fever."

"Jesus, Mary and Joseph, not a fever," said Karolina, horrified. "When pigs get a fever, it's all up with them. Your father will be pleased."

"We must get him out of this damned cage. If he can get on his feet outside, he'll find the roots and plants he needs."

With a stone I knocked two boards out of the barrier. We dragged the sick animal across the shed to the door. The raised threshold that kept the snow out in winter gave us a lot of trouble. We had to lift the pig to get it out of the shed into the meadow. It didn't move. It didn't protest. It didn't even raise its head. Now and then it grunted softly.

We must give him time, I thought. He'll notice he's in the open and will look for plants. We must be patient.

After some time Strobel still didn't move. From time to time I felt his brow. It seemed to be getting hotter and hotter. Perhaps the sun wasn't good for him. We dragged the animal into the shade of the wall that enclosed the meadow.

"We ought to cool his brow." With an old hat I fetched water from the spring and poured it over his ears. Strobel grunted and tried to lift his head. I kneeled down and tried to help him, but he couldn't get up. I held his hot head on my lap and talked to him. Mother always talked to the animals. To all of them, even pigs. She said pigs were intelligent, you just had to give them attention. "Karolina," I said, "the animal can't get up. Perhaps ice packs will help. I'll get some from the glacier." Without waiting for her answer I took my rucksack and pick and set off. I shouted to her to keep an eye on the cattle.

In one place dirty ice glistened below the scree. I hacked out some lumps. One was so big I had to break it up to get in into the rucksack. With the dripping sack I hurried back down the moraine.

The cattle were grazing near the hut. Karolina stood beside the sick pig. Strobel was still alive. I broke up the ice. Karolina threw the pieces into the jute sack I used to keep the rain off in bad weather. We laid the cold pack on the animal's head. It didn't try to stop us. Once it moved its stiff legs. I thought the ice-pack was already working. But nothing else happened.

Strobel lay by the wall and still did not move. "He's going to die," I thought. "I must go to Father! Perhaps he knows how to help the animal. If I run down to the valley now, I'll reach the village before nightfall. I can be back at dawn."

"And what about me? What am I to do? You can't leave a woman alone on this godforsaken mountain."

"Why not? I hope you're not afraid?"

"Of course I'm afraid! Would you like to spend the night here alone?"

"If I wait till the morning, it'll be too late. I've got to tell Father. I'm sure you'll survive one night. Sleep in the stable with the cattle."

"Well then, go. Bring two loaves and some salt. And maize. The sugar's all gone as well."

"I'll be back before sunrise."

Karolina passed me the wet rucksack. I ran down towards the valley.

When I reached Zermatt, the lights were already on in the hotels. The store in the upper village was still open. I bought bread, maize, salt and a little sugar. That is, I had it all put on our account. Father settled with them from time to time. He complained about the high bills and suspected the sales girls of writing down more than we had spent. But that was not true. They were more likely to forget to scribble something down than to enter something twice. When he had the money, Father paid regularly. When he did not, the owner had to bide his time.

I stepped through an iron gate into a chicken run. Steps hewn into the rock led to a small landing. The door was made of rough wood and the window was unglazed.

I opened the door. Father was sitting in front of his open bureau. The soft light of a paraffin lamp weakly lit the room. In front of him were the nickel and silver coins representing his day's income. He depended entirely on tips. All the same, he earned not much less than a mountain guide. Rainy days were always the best for him. In his lilting voice he would describe the many climbing accidents so vividly that the guests were genuinely affected, gaining new respect for the dangers of the mountains. This always brought something in.

In younger years he had been much in demand as a guide.

In 1893 Mr. H.F.B. Lynch took him on a very hazardous trip through Armenia. They were two months in the saddle. The long, dangerous rides through wild regions inhabited by Kurdish tribes were exactly to his taste. Father always had a Winchester repeating rifle loaded with sixteen cartridges slung over his shoulder. A Turkish dagger was also to hand. On 19 September 1893 he stood with his employer on the top of Mount Ararat.

Two years later he married Maria Julen. Maria was a delicate creature. She had weak lungs, as people used to say. Nevertheless, she bore him a son. On Candlemas Sunday she put their baby son to bed beside him. "Look after the child, I'm going to early mass," she said. Maria did not come home. She died in the church during the mass. The dead woman was carried to her parents, who lived next to the church. Father had many sisters. Katharina came to stay with him and did the housekeeping. The boy was only one year old, and sickly.

In 1898 Father was again engaged as guide to a mountaineering expedition. Mr. and Mrs. Bullock-Workman wanted to climb the Great Kabru in the Himalayas. With a caravan of about seventy people they were caught in bad weather and had to turn back on the glacier. The bearers had sailcloth shoes. They had to sleep in frozen woollen blankets instead of tents. The expedition had been inadequately prepared.

When he returned, his dead wife called her son, who suffered from the same illness as she, to join her. Father was alone again. He worked as a mountain guide. With his guests he climbed countless peaks between the Dolomites and Mont Blanc.

He married my mother in those years. The colour came back into his life. Rudolf remained a self-willed but very popular guide.

He always had enough work. When Miss Anny Peck wanted to engage him for a climb of Mount Huascaran, Peru, in 1908, Barbara advised him to stay at home. She had already brought two children into the world and could not understand why he should take such a risk. But Father was drawn by the adventure. He could not resist the lure. Unknown mountains had a hold on him. Wit his fellow guide Gabriel he left Zermatt to travel to the Andes via New York.

For months, Barbara heard nothing from him. The time he was expected to return was long past. A report on an expedition to the Andes went round the daily papers. A high mountain had been climbed for the first time. But the climbers had been overtaken by bad weather just below the summit.

The postmaster brought the cutting to Barbara. She was dreadfully worried. Why were no more details known? A sister-in-law embroidered a wall-hanging with the words:

"Though your last anchor rope may tear,

Do not despair."

At the end of October my mother got her first news. A telegram from Brig, a town not far off. Gabriel asked for a stretcher. They arrived in Zermatt by train. Father had open wounds. On 2 September 1908 they had reached the north peak of the Huascaran. As they climbed down, one of Father's leg-bands came undone. To re-tie it he took off a glove and wedged it under his arm. A storm gust made him almost lose his footing. When he tried to grab the glove with his stiff fingers, the wind tore it from his grasp and send it spinning into the void. In appalling weather conditions the descent continued. He had to use his pick with a bare hand.

Three weeks later, in the paupers' hospital at Yungay, a hut with a clay floor, the frostbitten parts were amputated: one foot and the fingers of his left hand. Anaesthetics were unknown to the doctor. Father was allowed to drink from a brandy bottle to survive the operation half-conscious on a simple table. The Indian nurse, who gave him his food with her bare hands, buried the severed parts in the nearby garden, so that they would rise again with all the others on the Last Day, she said.

Father paid no attention to me. In the weak light of the paraffin lamp he piled up his takings in little towers of one franc each, counted them and noted the total in an exercise book. I closed the door behind me. Only then did he notice me. He leapt up from his chair:

"What are you doing here at this hour? Is something wrong?"

Without waiting for an answer, he kissed me. He always kissed us on the mouth. I could never get used to it, but let him do it. He easily took offence.

"Strobel is ill. The pig with the light patch on his nose. He's got a fever. Yes, its' bad."

I had to tell him in detail how it all had happened, not even forgetting the weasel. He listened attentively.

"Bad news," he said when I had finished. "There's not much to be done for the animal. We're going to lose it. We'll miss its meat in the winter."

"Should I go to the quack, do you think?"

"Yes, we could do that. He may be able to give us some advice."

Anton lived in the Vehgasse. The farmers claimed he had good remedies for humans and animals. We went to see him. He was at home. Anton listened attentively.

"The pig's probably got bad food-poisoning. A strong purgative might help," he advised. "But who's going to give it to him? He'll resist. Perhaps even bite."

"Karolina would help me. But I don't know how to administer it."

Anton explained: "The animal must lie on its side. Someone must hold its head. The best thing is to wedge a round log between its teeth. That way it can neither bite nor shut its mouth, and you can pour the liquid down its throat. Naturally, not all at once. It must be able to breathe in between. But it's going to thrash about and kick."

Father paid for the bottle and gave it to me.

"The animal needs the medicine straight away," said the quack.

"All right. I'll be at the pasture at dawn."

"At dawn! That's too late. It needs the stuff now."

I looked at Father in alarm. I had not reckoned with having to go back up the mountain alone on this dark night. Father cleared his throat:

"It's impossible for me to come with you. It's the middle of the high season. I have to unlock the Museum at 8 o'clock."

For a moment no-one said anything. Then I admitted in a quavering voice:

"I... I'm afraid. It's pitch dark outside."

"Afraid? What of?"

"Of... ghosts. The dead."

"The dead have never done anyone any harm."

"People who've met them don't talk like that. Felix Blatter's hair went snow-white. And Johannes Seematter lost his speech. He stuttered for a long time. He had talked to a dead person."

"That's just people talking."

"With all the places that path passes, it would put the wind up anyone. You know all those places with spooky goings-on. And in the middle of the night, too. I'm scared!"

"In half an hour the moon will rise," prophesied the quack. "It'll light up the valley for you."

"A half moon!" I retorted defiantly.

"You can have my storm lantern. It's taken me all over the mountains," said Father. "I'll make you a present of it."

"No, no. That's the last thing I want. Lanterns stop your eyes adapting to the dark. You only see a few metres. You don't see anyone standing in the path. And they see you coming from a long way off."

"Who sees you coming?" laughed Anton.

I did not answer. It was useless. It was clear to me that I had to go back up the mountain that godforsaken night. What I had to do was really frightening. Father understood that. He had had his own experiences of ghosts. It tormented him to have to send me that long way back, but he saw no alternative.

"Come on," he said. "Let's go to the grocer's. I'll buy you something nice to take with you."

The ghost path

Father lent me his climbing stick. He probably thought it would give me confidence. With my rucksack slung over my shoulder and a roll and a sausage in my hand, I disappeared beyond the last street-lamp into the darkness of the night. Only slowly did my eyes grow accustomed to the path, the worn stones like bald heads under my nailed shoes, the turf beside the track and the weathered boards of the fence. The fenceposts were like a row of dwarfs along the road.

The moonlight foretold by the quack filtered wanly through the clouds. Now and then the cloud edges gleamed like silver, or with delicate rainbow colours, and sent a pale gleam into the valley. A thunderstorm was brewing. "If only I can get to the pasture before it bursts!"

The three abandoned sheds at Aermiete, about which there were so many stories, showed up like ghostly shadows. The path led close by their open doors. "Why do people always have to leave doors open? Not very pleasant for someone who has to pass them in the night, within range of a grabbing arm. Just a barn door banging can frighten a person to death."

Strain my eyes as I might, I could see nothing in the darkness of the open doorways. The first, the second, the third dark hole. You could not keep an eye on all of them at once. At the second you were threatened from three sides. As anyone knew, deserted stables were a veritable breeding ground for ghosts.

I glanced back over my shoulder as I had passed the last stable. To turn your back on the ghosts is a nerve-racking feeling. How easily they could catch you up!

At the Aerdbrich cross, just before the path forks to Zumsee or Zmutt, I thought I heard noises. Nocturnal walkers had often had stones thrown at them here. The stones hit the ground exactly in front of the toe of your shoe or behind the heel, so accurately were they aimed. But no-one was ever hurt. Nor was anyone seen. Often you heard a horrifying laugh as a macabre little extra.

There it was again, that squeaking. I heard it clearly. Or was it a shrieking? Fear took hold of me. The path was not fenced. To the left was a rocky slope down to the Zmuttbach. I tried to stay in the centre of the track and to hasten my steps. I was hardly fifty metres beyond the fork when I saw swaying lamps and bent figures coming round a projecting rock on the lower path. I caught my breath. "Jesus! The Ridge Party!"

In the meagre light I could see men with a mule hauling a sledge on which lay a dark heap. I heard them coughing and wheezing. "My God, they're taking accident victims down to the valley. There are dead bodies on the sledge. I know those carts." How often such cargoes had shaken me, even in daylight. I sometimes thought about them for weeks afterwards. The funeral procession was not calculated to give me new heart. I thought of joining the men and returning to Zermatt with them. For a few heartbeats I stood still. The procession disappeared behind a ridge. I was alone again. Alone in the darkness. And even more afraid. But I had to go up the mountain! I couldn't leave Strobel in the lurch. I must not falter now! What would Father say?

The first steps are always the hardest. I walked as quietly as possible, trying not to knock against stones with my nailed shoes or my stick, to avoid any unnecessary noise, to attract no-one's notice. Meanwhile my eyes scanned the path ahead, flicked right to the scree then quickly behind me.

Why do you always have to meet the dead when you are alone? And why do they only show themselves in the dark? In daylight it would not be half as bad. They could stay in their favourite haunts. Derelict old houses, lumber rooms, deserted mills, bridges and dilapidated fences. In daytime you could help them better. Set them free with promises. Or banish them to another place.

Exorcism is a harrowing experience. My uncle Basil once had a ghost in his apartment. It wasn't a wicked spirit, but it disturbed the peace of the household. Too many things got inexplicably lost: half a ham, a full bottle of schnapps for the morning coffee, a new penknife and countless other small utensils. The ghost was an obsessive collector. Something had to be done. Uncle Basil enlisted the help of a monk who was known far and wide for his piety.

At the midnight hour the monk attempted to draw the ghost out of the apartment and down to the graveyard. With Latin prayers and invocations he got it down the staircase and as far as the church. But when it saw the graves, the ghost clung to the balustrade of the Triftbach bridge. The holy man's Latin was to no avail. No biblical text or curse seemed to have any effect. In desperation he hurried to the churchyard gate, dipped his whole hand into the holy water font and copiously sprinkled the ghost. That helped. The spirit's strength was broken. It knew where it belonged and allowed itself to be banished to a grave. No-one was allowed to know which grave it was. But the holy man was said to have sworn never to get involved with another ghost in his whole life. It had been appalling, he said.

I did not have any holy water to hand. And the exorcising prayers were unknown to me. A walking stick would make no impression on a ghost. Periodically the half moon moved into the clear sky between the banks of cloud, and lit up for moments the treetops and crags. This constant alternation of light and shade brought disquiet and confusion to the silent forest. I reached the "Arufluh", which had spelled doom for many a nocturnal wanderer. The track, flanked by stone walls, left little room to pass if you had the misfortune to meet a different Rescue Party there: a funereal procession of poor souls seeking their salvation. Atoning for their sins, they would move with dragging feet, as only the dead move, along the narrow lane towards the glacier, their faces rigidly staring. To press against the wall while the dead people passed a hair's breadth away would be a terrible trial for even the strongest nerves. I should not have survived it. I should have trembled uncontrollably. I should certainly have dropped my stick, a dead person would have tripped over it and grabbed me for support. Stared at me without moving an eyelid. Taken me with him, with his gaze from eternity. You can meet familiar faces in the procession. Grandfather and his sweetheart, who had drowned herself; or you could meet someone you were in conflict with before their death. Now, suddenly, he's in front of you! Looking at you with blank, dim eyes.

A friend taught me how to address the dead: "In the name of Jesus Christ, what can I do for the salvation of your soul? Speak!" I would never get the words out. At the first syllable my mouth would drop open. I'm sure I would never be able to shut it again.

If someone passes you and you don't know him, yet he resembles someone close to you, then that figure is you. Your soul is already walking with the dead. It is only a question of hours and you will depart this life. Your own soul has had the grace to warn you!

"Jesus, what's that?" Above the path, in a clearing in the wood, a farmer had used for his own purposes a stony slope that did not belong to him. The rotten trunks of trees he had illegally felled lay about. He himself was long dead and buried; and where his soul finished up you can well imagine! Near the half-rotted wood a light was kindling! I saw it clearly. It did not flicker. It did not burn. A fluorescent, blue-green brightness, like the light of a hundred glow-worms. A light from another world! A deathly light! It smelled of putrefaction! Of tree-stumps and other things. How lucky that the path led past a stone's throw away. At the slightest breath of wind I could feel the cold sweat on my brow.

After the wood the path led past meadows. A number of sheds stood near it. Bats fluttered close to my head. On such nights even a mouse can frighten you. But the dreaded procession did not appear. It was not abroad that night.

Gradually my fear subsided. Or I imagined it did. My step grew lighter on the stony path. Soon the first houses of Zmutt must appear. There was just a sharp, zigzag climb between two rocks ahead of me.

Then it happened! A man was standing by the path. Where there was normally an old tree-stump, there he stood. I might not even have noticed him had he not stared motionlessly at me with wide saucer-eyes. I felt my pulse beating in my temples. My first reaction was: Run away! But it was too late. He could easily have overtaken me. And my position would have been even worse. "To run away is the worst thing you can do to a poor soul. It means you don't want to help him. You're a coward. I must go past him. Anything else spells ruin."

I looked apprehensively into the big, goggling eyes. At the extreme edge of the path, noiselessly, without touching the smallest pebble with my shoes or stick, I edged past in the darkness. Luckily the clouds lent me their shadow.

"May God have mercy on our soul!" I stuttered. "May God..." Then something terrifying happened. There were wingbeats, two, three. J could clearly hear the flapping of wings. It was no hallucination. As surely as I stand here now! I looked in terror over my shoulder. The ghostly eyes had gone. The treestump with its knotty roots was to be seen again. The figure with the bulging round eyes had disappeared from the face of the earth." Released, perhaps, by my prayer. Have I set a poor soul free? Helped it to reach heaven? The wing-beats had been very clear!"

No lights were burning in the little village of Zmutt. The few paraffin lamps had long been extinguished. I didn't want to pass along the narrow alley between the houses and stables. I had my reasons. But I also wanted to avoid the old path with walls on either side overgrown with prickly berberry bushes. I stepped into the mown meadows. Even though I stumbled into a furrow now and then, this seemed the lesser evil, as compared to running the ghost gauntlet. From the Bodmen pasture on I was in the territory of the Kalbermatte ghost. He was more familiar to me. I knew his sins, knew what he had to expiate. I was less afraid. All the same, I hoped that with the help of the saints in heaven he would leave me in peace.

It was past midnight when, bathed in sweat and exhausted, I reached the Kalbermatte. The door of the hut was not bolted. That meant Karolina was in the stable. I kept clear of the hut. The little window next to the stable door was dimly lit. Karolina was asleep on the straw. The burning lantern hung on the wall. With a sigh I shoved the door shut behind me: "Thank God for that! I'm back! It was awful!" I sat down on the floor next to Karolina. "Awful, I tell you. How is Strobel?"

"He's lying there. Take a look."

In the meagre light I saw the animal. His four legs were stuck out.

"But... But... he's dead!"

"Yes. He died just after you left."

"No!" I shouted, touching Strobel, who already felt cold. "It's not possible!" My sweaty brow touched the cold head of the dead beast. "All for nothing." I sobbed... and sobbed.

The storm

Someone took me by the shoulder. Still half asleep, I heard Karolina's voice.

"You mustn't sleep like that. It's too dangerous. The pig may have died of somthing infectous.

I was utterly dejected. Sitting on the straw. I felt Karolina pull my coat. I fell backwards and finished with my head resting against her breast. She ruffled my sweaty hair. It was good to be understood by someone. I felt her breath on my forehead. We lay silently in the half-dark. Her breast rose and fell. Her bodice smelt of dew-damp hay. Sleepily I looked up at the hanging lantern swaying slightly in the night breeze that came through a narrow gap beside the door. The windows were dark with soot. The shadow of the lamp's metal frame swayed across the ceiling. A big spider was crawling towards the lamp. "I can't sleep," I said.

"You can sleep anywhere if you want to," Karolina replied. The cows were breathing heavily. Sometimes they sighed or shook their heads, jangling their bells. The pig that was still alive grunted now and then, half-asleep. Two moths danced around the lamp. Karolina tried to press herself against me. I felt her leg between my knees.

"Stop it! You know I don't like that."

I sat up and put my arms round my knees. I dozed. Why do women always want to press our heads against their breasts? Unmarried Melanie in Aroleid often took me on her lap. Then she took barley-sugar out of her drawer. I was allowed to take a good-sized chunk, but she pressed my head against her breast and spoiled the pleasure of sucking the sweet.

"I'm going back to the hut," I said after a while. "The goats are so restless. Perhaps the weasel is nearby."

"It won't come as long as we're here."

"Why not? The animal's very trusting in the dark."

"I'm coming too." She stood up and brushed the straw from her clothes. "Please help me carry the dead pig out of the stable."

She got hold of its back legs. Together we dragged it outside and laid it near the wall. "It's better not to leave it with the healthy animals. Tomorrow I'll skin it."

"We can't do much with the meat, can we?"

"No."

"Pity. We haven't eaten any meat for such a long time." Karolina looked up at the night sky.

"It's completely clouded over. Not a star to be seen. I think there'll be a storm."

A fierce wind swept round the corner of the house. At the far end of the valley, in the basin around the Schönbühl cabin, long forks of lightning were darting. In the flashes you could see the border between the glacier and the moraine. When there was no lightning, it was pitch dark.

Karolina walked ahead with the lantern. It was only twenty paces to the hut.

"You go in first. There may be someone inside."

"Rubbish. Give me the lantern."

Compared to the accommodation in the stable, the hut was quite cosy.

I had devised a simple method of bolting the door. A thick beam could be wedged into holes in the walls. I just had to cut it to size and fit it into the holes. The stake fitted snugly against the door and made it impossible to open it from outside. Karolina turned down the wick of the stable lantern. The light flickered and expired. We undressed in the dark. You didn't need light to take off your trousers and hang them on a nail. Wearily I crept under the woollen blanket and nestled into the straw mattress. Karolina had undressed too. She undid the long plaits she wore wound round her head during the day. The comb she ran a few times through her hair had some teeth missing. With her hair hanging over her shoulders she stood beside the bed.

Perhaps she was saying a prayer her mother had once taught her.

The far-off lightning lit up the little windows. The wind was now blowing in violent gusts. It was bringing the storm closer. Then the first clap of thunder pealed outside. Rain and hail drummed on the slate roof and the west wall of the hut.

"Jesus, I'm scared!" shouted Karolina. "We're going to be struck. Disasters always come together!"

Because one of our animals had died, the hut was to be struck by lightning as well.

"Don't stand on the floor. In bed nothing can happen to you. Lightning has never yet struck a bed," I said to calm her. "Good night."

Again the thunder crashed outside the hut. The wind drove the rain against the windows. It drummed against the walls. From every direction water splashed on stones, slabs and tin cans. Small stones rolled from the roof. Then came a crash of thunder that made the hut tremble. One tongue of lighting after another flashed into the earth. The mountains threw the sound from side to side of the narrow valley. It seemed as if the rumbling would never die down. Each crash was followed by another still more deafening. Even with my eyes shut I could see the fluorescent light through my lids. There was a smell of sulphur and stone.

Only now did I notice that Karolina was kneeling on the bed. Her hair dishevelled on her back and her breasts hanging through the slit in her nightdress, she was stretching her arms towards me and screaming incoherently. Her voice was drowned by the thunder. I almost got up to calm her. But her big breasts and her stupid gesticulation put me off. Why should the lightning land specially on us? We had nothing metal to attract it. The cast-iron stove? That certainly wouldn't do it. I was reassured to think the pick and axe were in their proper place by the cheese vessel.

At last the storm passed on as it had arrived. The grumbling of the thunder grew fainter. The rain stopped. A pinkish light flickered along the valley. You could only hear the gutters and the torrent, where boulders were rolling. "Lie down, it's all over," I said to comfort her. She did not answer. From time to time I heard a quiet sobbing, like the sound of a child that has been beaten. How can anyone be so afraid of a thunderstorm? She had gone completely berserk.

Perhaps I ought to have shown more concern for her. With such ideas drifting through my mind my eyelids gradually closed and sleep took me in its arms.

The pasture was 2105 metres above sea-level. The altitude and the confined space often caused me to have confused dreams. I saw myself quite alone in the village square at Zumsee. Beyond the hillside rose the massive flank of the Matterhorn. You could see its shoulders and its white peak. Suddenly the mountain turned into an old man's head with bushy eyebrows and a flowing white beard. This mighty head looked at me with kindly eyes and nodded. It nodded twice, thee times. That was all that happened. It said nothing. Not a word. And I had no idea what it meant. But I was aware that the Matterhorn wanted to tell me something very important. It remained a secret. All the same, I was overjoyed and full of ease, as one can only be in a dream.

At that moment I heard a cry, very close. Immediately I was wide awake. I leapt out of bed. The widow above Karolina's feet was brightly lit. The sliding pane was open. An arm was poking through, groping for Karolina's legs. Only then did I notice faces behind the windows, beside a burning lantern. I knew them. It was the Bettmingers, father and son.

Karolina had pulled her legs up. She was sitting on the bed, trembling all over, although she could see it was people from the neighbourhood, not ghosts, who had grabbed her feet as she slept. The two men were laughing, thinking themselves clever to have frightened Karolina so much.

"It's the Bettmingers," I said. "They want a drink. I'll get dressed." I slipped my trousers on. Karolina, too, crept out of bed. When the men took the lantern from the window, she got dressed. I pulled the wedge from the door and opened it. The lantern burned on the stone table. The two guides were in buoyant mood.

"It was cruel of you to frighten Karolina like that", I said. They weren't impressed. On the contrary, they went on laughing and joking. The low wall that served as a seat was wet. They could not sit down. I fetched a dry shelf from the cheese-making corner.

Young Bettminger said: "You scared us far more. As we were coming along the wall in the dark, I stumbled over a body! First I thought the devil had grabbed me by the legs. Thought I was a goner – I scared my father with my scream. He lit the place with the lantern and we found a dead pig. Sorry about the animal, you've been unlucky."

I just nodded. I didn't want to talk about it. Old Bettminger noticed this. He grumbled:

"We're wet through. The storm caught us out all right. Can we have some hot coffee?"

Karolina stood by the door. She had regained her composure. Where men were concerned, she didn't bear grudges.

"I'll brew you some nice coffee," she said obligingly.

"We've traversed the Matterhorn. The Zmuttgrat was iced over. If it had been any worse, we'd have been stuck on that damned ridge. By the way, your mother sends her greetings. She said you should visit her some time."

"Thanks. How is she?"

"Fine, I think. She had no time to chat. Her kitchen was buzzing like a hive."

Karolina brought the coffee. The men joked with her and invited her to drink with them. She sat between the two.

"You were lucky the middle window was so well fixed," the young man teased her. "Perhaps we can put that right another time?"

She was already giggling again.

Old Bettminger pulled a flask from his rucksack. Soon the hut smelled of schnapps and coffee. Lightning still flickered behind the Gornergrat, but over our valley there were already gaps in the clouds. The crescent moon appeared and cast a silvery light over the pasture. Who would have thought that such a storm had just swept down the valley? The Bettmingers sang, with much comic miming, the song of the Polish Maid.

Karolina was in high spirits, flirting with the guides. Suddenly I began to shiver. "The boy should be in bed," said old Bettminger. "And we must be on our way. We've a lot to do tomorrow."

"Do you think you'll meet my father?"

"I can call on him. About the dead pig?"

"Yes. I was in the village last night. Fetched some medicine. All for nothing. The pig was dead when I got back."

"Pigs are awkward to help when they're ill."

"Father will be annoyed."

"He will that, but don't feel bad about it. Things like that can happen to anyone."

"It all happened so quickly."

"I can imagine how you feel. Well then, see you later."

They went on down the path. All we could see was their lantern swinging down the valley.

The torrent

The pasture bloomed. From every slope came a golden sunny glow. In the crevices between the rocks sunrose spread in patches of unbroken colour. Arnica, verbena and digitalis scattered their strong yellow across the slopes and hills. Sweetwilliam, snapdragon, moraine rose, forget-me-not and bluebell added tints from pale pink and deep mauve to light and dark blue. It was the season of flowers, colours and giddy insects. Anything that had wings and a snout to suck nectar went fluttering drunkenly across the meadow.

I too was seized by a desire to roam the mountains. I kept looking up towards the crest of the Hörnli. In the soft morning air the smoke rose from the chimney of the Matterhorn cabin. A thin swathe of vapour hung over the roof. Mother was sure to be at the stove cooking for all the hungry tourists. The wish to visit her and feel her anxious love grew stronger and stronger. I had to see her.

I left at sunrise. I wanted to avoid the detour over the moraine of the Zmutt glacier. Between Kalbermatte and Stafelalp there was no bridge over the torrent. All the same, I intended to take this route. It was naive of me. A challenge to the wild water, but I had often resolved to rush in a straight line from the Kalbermatte across the Stafelalp to the Hörnli cabin. Now I was to put the plan into practice.

"Where are you off to?" called Karolina, when she noticed I was not taking the usual path.

"I'm crossing the stream." I took the board we used as a seat when the wall was wet in rainy weather.

"Are you mad? You'll drown! Do you hear – you'll be killed and I'll get the blame!" she shouted after me. I waved to her. Behind the wall of the crescent-shaped pasture I ran down to the stream.

In the early morning the water-level in the Zmuttbach was quite low. A boulder stuck its round head out of the water in the middle of the raging stream. I shoved the board out to it. It made a very narrow, unsteady bridge. At every step the board tilted to one side or the other. I balanced myself carefully above the racing water. The board bent more and more. The foam was already splashing my shoes. I was only two or three steps from the end. Then the board tilted so far that I lost my balance and was on the point of falling into the torrent. With a desperate leap I reached the rock. But I did not grasp it in the middle, but on one side where the stream was already splashing over it. The icy water filled my shoes. First I had to get over my shock. Somewhere between my neck and my chest I felt my pulse hammering. "I've been damned lucky," I thought. "And the board is still there. Without that I'd be stuck."

Even at this early hour the torrent foamed and thundered like an avalanche into the valley. I stood on the boulder and considered the second half of the crossing. The other bank was higher. A large rock stuck out its tongue at me. Was it teasing me or just trying to help in some mineral way? I first had to pull the board after me, then push it cautiously on to this rock. It was a dangerous balancing act. The torrent snatched at the board and tried to dislodge me from the boulder. On no account could I let go of the board. "My God, I'd have no chance of ever getting away. By midday the torrent would cover the rock." Such thoughts as these ran through my mind as I struggled with the board on the slippery rock. When the plank came to rest on the projecting rock, I laid the other end on the boulder. I had not thought of bringing stones with me to wedge it. So the board rocked at both ends. Very cautiously I edged along it, standing sideways. Again the board bent. Spray from the stream had caught the board, making it very slippery. To go forward became more and more dangerous. I tried another leap. But the board was too slippery. My nailed shoes skidded as I pushed off. I missed the bank and fell into the stream. Luckily my shoes found some hard foothold for a second leap. Still ankledeep in water I fell on gravel and scrambled on to the bank. The board had bounced off the boulder as I jumped. It was seized by the torrent. Savaged by the boiling water, it was tossed from side to side and vanished into the gorge.

I sat down on the root of a pine, undid my shoes and poured the water from them. I took off my socks and wrung them out. It was relieving to sit there watching the raging torrent and being thankful to be alive. Only now did I notice Karolina on the other side of the stream. She was waving her arms about, pointing to her forehead, shaking her fist and shouting something to me. It was impossible to make out her words. The din of the water drowned everything. But I could imagine what she was saying. I nodded to her. For once we agreed. She pointed to the stream. Was she lamenting the lost board? Or was she pointing out that the same thing could have happened to me? I put on my shoes, waved to her cheerfully and ran up into the wood.

At the Stafelalp Hotel a young maid was standing outside the main door cleaning shoes. Half-asleep, she was surprised to see me hurrying past the house so early.

I took the direct route to the cabin. First across the pastures of the Stafelalp, then over rubble and rocks to the Hörnli crest and then zig-zag up to the hut.

Mother was sitting at a long kitchen table. She was writing something on a piece of paper, lost in thought. When she saw me, she stood up in surprise and came towards me. I ran into her arms. She kissed me on the cheeks and forehead. Then she laughed: "You haven't washed yourself too thoroughly this morning, I see." I did not mention that I had not been to the well with soap and towel for weeks. "The main thing is you're here," she said. "I'll go and get you a good breakfast."

While I ate, the cabin warden and the waitress sat down with me. Mother wanted to hear about everything. "How are you getting on with Karolina? Is she a good girl? Can she make cheese? Is she selling much milk to tourists? Is she writing down her takings in the little book I gave her? And you? Are you bored? You've no-one to play with! No-one to talk to!"

"Yes, I have."

"Who's that?"

"The… the mountains."

"The mountains? You look at them closely?"

"No, I talk to them."

Veronika, the waitress, stole a glance at Mother. "You can't talk to mountains."

"Yes, you can. Not always. Sometimes they don't want to. Perhaps because the night was too cold. Or a thunderstorm has upset them."

"If that's all it is," said the waitress.

"I like talking to them. Only when they're angry, then I don't. I leave them in peace."

"Oh, they're angry sometimes, are they?" said the warden in a teasing voice. "Why?"

"How do I know? Perhaps because they've been climbed by someone they don't like. Sometimes the Matterhorn plays with a long strip of cloud like a scarf," I laughed. "Or it pulls a wool cap over its ears and asks me if I think it looks funny."

The warden, in his size 12 shoes, cleared his throat and laughed: "You've been reading too many fairy stories."

Veronika, the waitress, was more curious: "How do the mountains talk? I mean, can you hear what they're saying?"

"Of course. You just mustn't be afraid. I mean, when they send a fall of rock or ice into the valley. Otherwise they laugh at you. You have to trust them."

"And you trust them," the warden mocked.

"Of course. I'll climb them all when I'm a guide."

Mother found the conversation rather embarrassing. She knew that life on the high pasture with a maid and no playmates had its problems. This weighed on her. She sighed: "Don't forget to eat, my boy. In the autumn you'll have your school friends again."

Happily the conversation took a different turn, otherwise I should have finished up explaining that I also talked to the sun, said "Good morning" to it, asked it the time, said goodbye in the evening, sometimes even played tricks on it. It went like this: I would take my leave of it when it went down behind the jagged crest of the Dent Blanche. Then I ran up a nearby hill that was still bathed in sunlight and met it with a laugh: "Here I am again. Surprised, are you? You see, we live on a hump-backed world." And we said goodbye again. The sun went down, a molten red sphere behind the crag. Long fingers of sunlight still reached into the valley, stretching after me, or trying to cling to the mountain crest like a spider.

It was not a real leavetaking. It was just saying goodnight, for in the morning he rose up like a miracle into the sky on the other side of the valley. And the game started all over again. The distance didn't matter. I could feel him. With hot fingers he touched my back, my chest, my legs, when I took off my shirt and rolled up my trousers.

Solitude sharpens our intuitions. We sense a new world. I often wanted to chastise myself, modelling myself on holy men. Perhaps to prove to myself in my loneliness that I was still there. Was still alive. Had a body that could feel sensations. I beat my bare back with juniper twigs. Not too hard. No, rather cautiously to feel the sharp needles not as pain but as a tickling.

Luckily I didn't mention any of that. They would have thought I was mad. Or venerated me as a saint. And I would have had to go on chastising myself and passing on the messages from the mountains.

"We have to get back to work," said Mother. "Everything will be starting up soon. The first tourists will be back from the Horn."

"And I'll run back to the Kalbermatte this afternoon."

"No, you won't, my boy. You'll stay with us today. You can sleep in my room. Karolina can manage the pasture on her own for two days, I'm sure."

I was happy.

The honeymoon

In front of the Hotel Belvedere and the cabin a terrace had been built on the rocky slope. From there you could see the mountaineers on the Horn with the naked eye. With a telescope you could make them out clearly. Tourists who had come up from the valley clustered round the telescope. They were all thirsty and wanted tea, soup or some other refreshment. I was allowed to help Veronika wait on them. Many tourists sat in the sun and unpacked their picnics from their rucksacks. I ran with beer bottles, mineral water and glasses from the kitchen to the tables. When Mother needed water for the stove, I had to fetch clean snow from north of the cabin in two big pails. She tipped it into a pan, where it melted at once.

The mule-driver came up the zig-zag path with his sure-footed beast. I helped him unload the two baskets full of food and drinks. Mother gave me some bread-crusts to reward the mule. I held it by its lead, wondering whether I ought not be a mule-driver rather than a guide. To go from Zermatt to the cabin every day with such a well-behaved animal must be a fine thing.

Suddenly my uncle Franziscus was standing beside me. He had climbed the Matterhorn with a visitor from Manchester. Franziskus was my favourite uncle. He could play merry yodelling songs on his dulcimer. "I heard the hotel has got a new manager", he said, teasing. "Can I have a pot of tea with some red wine in it?" I was proud to serve him.

There was constant commotion in front of the cabin. Ordering and paying. Looking, explaining and chatting. Mother hardly had time to exchange a word with me. About two o'clock she finally had a moment to have something to eat. Many tourists had gone down into the valley. Others were coming up the path with heavy rucksacks. They wanted to spend the night in the hotel or the cabin, then climb the Horn. Among them was the old mountain guide Lerjien from Täsch. He was particularly fond of banter. When he passed the Kalbermatte, he always shouted a few friendly words to me.

"So you've left your cows alone in the pasture, have you?" he joked.

"They'll come to no harm. I've tied them all up."

"That's how you treat your animals, is it? I know: you want to go up the Horn. I can see it by the tip of your nose."

"I want to all right, but I don't trust myself to do it alone."

"You can come with me. I'll tie you to my rope. Do you want to come?"

Did I want to? I was bowled over by the idea that he might mean it seriously. I rushed to Mother and implored her to let me go. Lerjien came too and assured her he was serious. Mother looked worried. She did not think much of the idea and couldn't make up her mind. Finally she agreed. Veronika gave me a pullover and gloves, as I wasn't wearing enough warm clothes. Lerjien was guiding a young Bavarian, who consented to having the cabin cook's boy attached to the rope. It all seemed to be going well. I couldn't wait for the next day. But then our neighbour, the guide Hieronymus, heard of my plan.

"Don't you do anything so stupid, my boy," he commanded.

"Let it be. You could over-strain yourself. Where would that leave you? With a heart defect for the rest of your life." He meant it well, I knew. All the same, I was disappointed. "I'll have to talk to your mother. Your father certainly wouldn't allow it." Hieronymus went into the kitchen. When Mother called me shortly afterwards, I knew she was going to withdraw her permission. Grudgingly I agreed. Old Lerjien consoled me, talking of another year. "I'll be sure to take you some time. We want to make a proper mountain guide out of you, don't we?"

That evening I stood a long time in front of the cabin. The first lights were twinkling in Zermatt. The Mischabel group glowed orange-red in the evening sun. The sky showed all the shades from delicate eggshell green to ink blue. Between the peak of the Dufour and the Liskamm stood the crescent moon. I looked long at the Matterhorn. It towered in the sky like smoky quartz. It was completely in the shade. A pale star sparkled above its peak. From the east face came the sound of falling rocks. The mountain only found peace on ice-cold nights. In the warm summer evenings it rumbled far into the night. From time to time short gusts of wind came over the crest. Perhaps Mother was right. Perhaps it was better to wait a year or two.

I went back into the kitchen. A few guests were packing their food supplies. They wanted to go to bed early. The guides were sitting at the long table chatting about their tours. They were really exchanging information: "How was the cliff of the Zmutt crest? Did you have to by-pass the Gendarm on the Rothorn? Was the Grenz glacier badly fissured? Did you see the rope I had to leave behind on a crampon on the 'Four Donkeys'?" And more in that vein. Lerjien had his pipe in his mouth. He gave me a long look, suppressing a smile. He probably wanted to tease me, but thought it better to let sleeping dogs lie. He gave me a kindly pat on the shoulder.

More guests came in. A gentleman and a pretty young blonde entered the kitchen in felt slippers. The people at the table squashed together to make room for them. They did not want to eat in the restaurant next door. "It's so cosy here in the kitchen," said the lady to Mother. "We like to be a bit snug. You see, we're on our honeymoon."

"On your honeymoon?" My mother was impressed. "And you want to go up the Matterhorn?"

"Yes, we've always wanted to. We're both mad about mountains, my husband and I. We couldn't think of anything better for our honeymoon."

Mother fetched a bottle of Dôle. "We must celebrate that with a glass of wine. Let's drink to your health and your future!" The guides treated the couple very cordially and there was soon a convivial gathering round the table. The men teased the lady for picking an overcrowded cabin dormitory for her wedding night. She was not short of apt retorts, which further heightened the merriment.

Mother pulled a worried face when she heard the couple intended to climb the mountain without a guide. "My husband's an experienced alpinist," said the blonde. "On the ascent he will be the leader. And when we come down, I'll go first."

How right the lady was. But she must have imagined the "coming down" rather differently.

Mother sent me up to her room. "Bedtime for you. Veronika and I must do the washing up. I'll come up as soon as I've finished."

"Are you going up too in the morning?" the blonde lady asked me.

"No, I'm not allowed to yet. I'm just visiting my mother."

"Oh, the boy's your son," she said. "Isn't he sweet?"

This embarrassed me. I looked down, drew circles with my finger on the table and cast a sidelong glance at my neighbours. It was a relief when Mother told me to hurry up to bed.

When Mother slipped into bed beside me, I must have been having a bad dream. Perhaps the altitude, too, was making me restless. I squashed against the wall. It was comforting to feel Mother near me, her soft curves and hollows. Her hair smelled of heather and her breath of fresh beeswax. Cuddling close to her, I soon fell deeply and peacefully asleep.

Suddenly I was roughly shaken. Mother was standing beside the bed. Through the windows came the early morning light. "You must get up at once, Hannes. Something dreadful has happened. The honeymoon couple have had an accident!" "The honeymoon couple?" I answered sleepily. "Yes, the nice lady and her husband. They've fallen. You must take a message down to Schwarzsee. They've got a telephone there." I was slow to grasp what had happened. But then I leaped into my trousers. I was dressed in a flash. Mother said I should not leave till I had had something to eat. "We can't help them any more. They're both dead, the poor things."

A guide had observed the accident. The woman had tried to step on to a rock to one side of the normal route. It had given way under her feet. She fell the same instant, dragging her husband, who was climbing in front of her, down a steep gorge on the east face.

The cabin warden, a guide called Aufdenblatten, and a doctor who happened to be on the scene tried to reach the bodies. Rock falls and icy patches of cliff made their progress difficult. When the party found the pair on a tongue of glacier at the foot of the east face, they looked like two sleepers. They lay quite close together, their hands stretching towards each other. Beneath their heads the ice was stained red. They seemed so be lying on a big red cushion. Their faces were not disfigured, but they were beyond help now.

The warden took the victims' names and addresses from the cabin register so that their families could be informed. He asked for a team of guides to be sent to recover the bodies. Taking the note, I rushed down the Hörnli path like a whirlwind to the Hotel Schwarzsee. Some people were already standing around the big telescope. From what they had observed, they knew there had been an accident on the mountain. Breathlessly I told them what had happened. I gave the message to the hotel manageress. Then I hurried back to the Stafelalp. I kept looking up to the Matterhorn, reproaching it bitterly. "Such nice people. They visit you on their honeymoon and you throw them down. And you want to be my friend?"

The Horn hid its face in a scrap of cloud. It was really ashamed of itself.

The Ridge Party

The strips of rock that ran diagonally down from the Hohlicht into the valley ended in a border of grassland along the Zmuttbach gorge. Lush pasture grew on this border. At its narrowest point the pasture was crossed by a wall built of loose stones.

The path to the Schönbühl cabin wound along the gorge. When it reached the wall, it passed through a doorframe slanted by the wind. A disintegrating wooden door hung from rusty hinges. It always fell shut when people went through. Most of them just gave it a kick with a nailed boot to open it. No-one was particularly gentle with it. It knew what people were like. To my animals it blocked the way to the pastures which were out of bounds.

The previous day there had been a violent thunderstorm. I drove the animals close to the wall. Rocks from the Titer had come down there and I wanted to inspect the damage. The little Titerbach had been blocked by rubble in places, overflowing its banks and depositing debris on the pasture. In one place the wall was damaged. I repaired it with stones that had fallen from the rockface.

The scented air lay delicate across the valley, and the mountains shone a dazzling white in the morning sun. There was fresh snow on the Zmutt glacier. Though I could feel no wind, the old door rattled continuously in its frame. An invisible hand pushed it a finger's breadth open, then let it fall shut again. Perhaps the invisible spirits of the Ridge Party were passing through it, opening the door just wide enough to slip through in their shrouds, then letting it bang shut again. The fresh snow on the glacier might have induced the poor souls to start their barefoot pilgrimage over the cold ice.

Karolina had inflamed my fantasies over the morning cup of milk. "I saw the Ridge Party," she said, "as sure as I stand here now." Actually, she was sitting on the low wall in front of the hut. "In the middle of the night. It was terrifying. They were going up the path towards the glacier, right above our hut." In those days every mountain-dweller still knew that poor souls had to wander barefoot over the icy glaciers, dressed only in their shrouds, to find mercy in the eyes of God. "Some of the dead had burning lanterns in their hands and swung them as they walked. Others had cloven hoofs like the Devil. Don't laugh! I saw it with my own eyes. They were dragging their mortal sins behind them on a horned sledge. How they sighed! Even the stones by the wayside shrieked, it was so eerie and wretched."

"Why didn't you wake me? I should have liked to see the Ridge Party too."

"Don't talk nonsense! Do you think I spent a long time looking at it? First of all I was rigid with fright. Then I ducked down under my blanket. I couldn't cross myself. I couldn't even move a finger. I hope I'll never meet the dead again. I wouldn't survive another Ridge Party. If I hadn't started to pray in my terror, I should have died. True as I stand here now!" She was still sitting. It wasn't like her to swear as volubly as this, so I was impressed by what she said.

As I was driving the herd over to the wall, I saw marks in the ground that must have come from a horned sledge. This was the name given to a special kind of sledge with long curved runners at the front like ram's horns. They were used to take mountain hay down to the valley in summer. The runners were not lined with metal and left distinctive tracks. "So there must have been some truth in the story," I thought.

Now and then I looked at the door that went on banging in its frame although there was no wind. Suddenly I heard two dull thuds. I looked up at the rocks at once. A boulder as big as a beer barrel was bounding down the slope. No time to worry about the herd! I vaulted over the wall and threw myself flat on the ground. There was a crash in the bed of the stream. The cow-bells jangled in panic. At the same moment I was drenched in ice-cold water. Then silence reigned again. I jumped up. The animals were standing about, staring distraughtly at the stream. The rock lay in the middle of the stream. It had landed so hard the water had splashed far and wide, wetting me as well. Luckily no animal had been hit. "It's not all down yet", I thought. "I must get away from here with the herd. If a chunk like that comes down, others can follow". I quickly drove the animals back to the enclosure. There they were protected from rock falls by a ridge supported by a ledge of rock.

The goats had had a lucky escape. The rock had made two deep craters in the turf where they were grazing. They had all fled to the ridge and were now rejoining the herd across the rocky ledge. Bilberry plants grew along the side of the path. It was pleasant to stretch out on them to dry your clothes.

Some hikers came past. My unkempt hair hung over my ears. A safety pin lengthened my braces and made up for a missing button. A lady pointed her camera at me, then went on her way with a kindly smile.

I lay on my back looking up into the depths of the cloudless sky and considering how I should tell my friends in Zermatt the story of the falling rock. It was clear to me that it should not end so harmlessly. As I pondered this, I heard from the jangling of cow-bells that the herd was in motion again. Looking up, I caught my breath. A group of mountaineers was coming down the steep track. A mule was dragging a horned sledge. Some of the men had tied short ropes to the sledge and were helping the animal to manoeuvre the load down the rocky path. Something longish was roped to the sledge: an accident victim. I jumped up and stood rooted to the ground. Uncle Peter-Martin was one of those pulling the ropes. The men were sweat-soaked and weary. They all were guides from the valley. There was a stranger with his arm in a sling. To my surprise the caravan stopped in front of me. The mule was wet, steaming. The sailcloth sheet wrapping the body showed big patches of dried blood. Climbing boots and brown stockings poked from the sheet at the back of the sledge. Uncle Peter-Martin came up to me. There was a strange look in his eyes. Almost inaudibly he said: "Josmarie's been killed – on the Long Ridge." For some inexplicable reason I asked: "My uncle?" He nodded. I turned away from the people. Peter-Martin put his hand on my shoulder. Then I heard them driving the mule again. The stones crunched. The men 's feet tramped. The caravan went on its way. I looked after it with wet eyes. I saw them disappear into a hollow. Then they followed the stony track along the gorge.

I drove the herd back to the pasture. Everywhere the track was marked by the runners. Avoiding them, I walked beside the path. It seemed disrespectful to walk between tracks carved by my poor uncle. You don't step over a coffin either. When I met Karolina I asked: "Did you see them? – Did you give them something to drink?"

"They wanted beer. I only had fresh milk."

"You didn't accept any money, did you?"

"I didn't want to, but the stranger with his arm in the sling pressed five francs into my hand."

After a while I said: "It was Uncle Josmarie they brought down."

"Your uncle? – My God, how dreadful! It was those men who frightened me in the night. The Ridge Party."

A rush of blood

Not far from the hut, on top of a knoll overlooking the valley, stood a large limestone rock. Its pinkish-white tint showed that it came from the Weissfluh, at the base of the Zendju Ridge. The glacier must have carried it there, then left it stranded. On this round-cheeked boulder stood a dwarf pine with a thatch of bushy needles. When you climbed the rock, you found parts smoothed by time and the weather. Between them were deep fissures, in which grew flowers and tufts of grass. On warm days a host of insects, beetles and butterflies danced around the rock. Caterpillars crawled up the grass stalks and ants had laid out a route from the base to the tree. Nearby, the Titerbach hopped down over the rocks, inviting you to play. Clouds with comic faces cast their shadows over the pine-rock, then let it shine again in the sun.

It was one of the joys of the shepherd's life to lie on the boulder next to the pine, chattering to the Matterhorn or looking dreamily into the sky and feeling oneself carried out over the valley by the ragged clouds. And if the solitude became too much, you could relieve your feelings by singing, yodelling or just letting out a delirious cry that brought a shocked response from the mute rock walls.

Now and then a glacier fall on the Matterhorn broke the silence, or a whooping cry from the Fair Helena rang across from the Stafelalp and was lost in the valley. The cliffs answered her yearning call. Only rocks could answer. Not even the Archangel Seraphin could have sent forth that "Yoo-hoo hooee" as fervently and as crystal-clear – assuming he was a "she" and not a male of the species, which you can never be sure of with angels. Fair Helena had much of the angel about her in the way she grew her hair, her bodily form and her long-limbed legs. But she didn't live in heaven, but in a sooty cabin on the Stafelalp.

And she slept in a bed of mortal sin. True, no-one knew who had brought this bed such notoriety. Perhaps it was just idle gossip. But the bed existed; I had seen it with my own eyes.

I had to borrow some salt for my animals. That was when Helena showed me the bed. First you entered a dingy kitchen. Before a small window stood an old table with stools around it. After a while, when your eyes had got used to the dark, you could see the fireplace at the other end. The cheese-vat hug on a chain from an iron bar. Scythe, rake, cloths, aprons and ropes hung on nails and hooks. Next to them a doorway led into the bedroom. Through three small, murky windows you could see the snow and ice of the Zmutt glacier. To the left of the door, near the small holy-water font, stood a massive, bandy-legged bed.

It was covered by a brightly-coloured, hand-woven bedspread. The fringes hung down at the sides, their tips touching the floor. It looked like a proper marriage bed. But it wasn't. It was a bed of mortal sin. Perhaps some braggart had tricked his way to the lonely woman's favours and bragged about it in the village. Men have sharp ears for such things.

Helena gave me a glass of milk. While we talked about the prevailing drought and the meagre pasture, I surreptitiously scanned the bed. On the heavy footboard many initials had been cut into the wood. A heart, or at least part of one, had been carved there too. Perhaps the knife wasn't sharp enough to finish the heart. Or love had not lasted long enough. Helena noticed my preoccupation with the bed. She was a mischievous creature.

"You like it – my bed of mortal sin?" she asked. I was deeply embarrassed. Blushing crimson, I found nothing to say and tugged at my jacket buttons.

"You'd like to try it out, I dare say," she teased.

"No!" I retorted vehemently. "Definitely not. Not me. I was just looking that way."

"I don't believe you. You're just saying that. I can see it in your eye."

"No, really, word of honour. I…" Words failed me. Helena laughed. She took my head and pressed my nose to her abundant bosom.

"I know, I know. You've got your Karolina, haven't you?" she said roguishly.

"That's not true. It's a rotten lie!" I had torn myself away from her.

Helena buried her fingers in my matted hair.

"Hey! Don't get so worked up, or you'll make me suspicious!"

Deeply irritated, I rushed back to the Kalbermatte as fast as I could.

Helena had touched a sensitive spot. Of course, I was having a kind of experience with Karolina, though it had nothing to do with a bed of sin. All the same, it was on my mind for weeks on end. I had no-one with whom I could have talked about it.

The smallness of our hut forced us to live in the closest proximity to each other. It was usually dark when we went to bed. That was good – it avoided problems. We never lit a candle. Pale twilight came through the windows. That was enough for us to find the nails to hang up our apron, dress and trousers. We both slept in our daytime vests. She undid her long black hair, let it fall about her shoulders and lifted herself on to her creaking bed. My straw couch was half underneath hers. My legs lay under her bed. Our heads were at different levels, but so close that I could hear every breath or sigh she uttered.

In the morning it was light in the hut. Karolina was first to crawl out of bed. She combed her hair, plaited it and wound it around her head in the style of little Verena on the coins. Was she beautiful? I don't know. She was old – about twenty-three. When she combed her hair, she bit the hairpins. She had a set of dazzling white teeth, like a wildcat's. Her snub-nose was covered with freckles. She did not have eyes, just two slits fringed with long dark lashes. When they were not dazzled by the sun, they glowed a mossy green. Aunt Magdalena had once warned me:

"Be careful of people with moss-green eyes. They're no good!"

She was right. The cheeses Karolina made were not what Father had expected. Some of them soon got as hard as flint, others swelled up, got soft and liquid and dripped from the hanging shelves that were supposed to protect them from the mice.

Karolina was convinced that she was a beautiful woman. Beside her bed hung a photo of her in a carved wooden frame. She was hardly recognisable. It was a picture of a gentlewoman. The photo had been taken when she was working as a kitchen maid for a doctor's family in Geneva. Perhaps the elegant clothes came from the wardrobe of the doctor's wife. Karolina's gloved fingers rested on the handle of a colourful umbrella. An oval pendant on a long gold chain dangled over her sinfully low décolleté. The *pièce de résistance* was an enormous hat with bushy feathers. It gave her the dignity of a true countess. What a contrast to the nailed shoes, thick wool stockings and home-woven skirt she wore at the pasture! Her short bodice jacket could be buttoned over her bosom, but Karolina left the top two buttons undone. When she bent down, her breasts shone white from beneath the dark-brown cloth of the jacket. Karolina did not know the difference between a bee and a wasp. But she knew all about her womanly charms. When young men sat down in front of the hut for a chat and a glass of milk, she fetched the picture from her bedside. "Take a look! Me in my Sunday best. Classy, aren't I? I bet you're surprised. That's Gaagla!" And she contemplated her picture with reverence.

In Törbel, her native village, at the mouth of the valley, they called her "Gaagla". This didn't sound very flattering to me, but it seemed to please her. In our dialect we say "Gaagu" for raven. As the raven is masculine, the word had to be put into the feminine form, which was "Gaagla". No doubt her jet-black hair was the reason they called her the "raven".

I had got used to her hair. When she rubbed it lightly with butter, it shone like the feathers of that croaking bird. But it was other hairs on her body that agitated me. They were still blacker, still more exciting.

In high summer the sun rose so early that it was already shining through the window when Karolina emerged from her bed. She first put her legs down over the side and took some time yawning heartily and stretching herself. Once, as she was slipping out of bed, the blanket got tangled with her nightdress and pulled it up to her waist. What then revealed itself was unexpected indeed. I could not believe my eyes. To see something so contradictory on a woman was more than a shock to me. A beam of sunlight from the window fell on her loins. The delicate white skin of her long thighs shone radiantly. But so did her frizzy, raven-black plume, which I saw for the first time on a woman. It seemed to me like a silly joke creation was playing with the delicate female form. On a man's tousled body an excrescence like that might just be understandable, but not on a woman. Any grandfather would have been proud of such a luxuriant beard; I had never seen moss grow so profusely on any pine. The discovery filled my thoughts for weeks. And I could not talk to anyone about it. Karolina noticed that I had something on my mind.

"What is it you've got against me?" she asked one day.

"Me? Nothing. What should I have? Women don't interest me, anyway."

"You sometimes give me such funny looks."

"I give you funny looks? Rubbish. Bettminger gives you funny looks. You should ask him."

Bettminger had been a frequent caller recently, stopping for a glass of milk and bantering with Karolina. He poured himself his own milk in the cellar, went in and out of the cabin and stable and acted like the owner of the pasture. The way he smiled at Karolina, gazed at her with glinting eye and embraced her at any opportunity had earned him my enmity. I did not know much about life, but I had noticed that for men the same rules did not apply when they met a woman in the village street as when they did so miles from any habitation.

We had run out of supplies. I used the Sunday to hurry down to Zermatt. Mother wanted me to attend Sunday mass from time to time. As I reached the first meadows, just above the Zmutt bridge, I met Bettminger. He had a spray of alpine roses in his hatband. He called to me:

"Is Gaagla at home?"

"She's got to mind the herd," I answered curtly.

"Fine, then I can help her," he laughed.

The way he said it, puckering his mouth and twinkling with his eyes, made me suspicious. He's up to something, I thought. Otherwise he wouldn't be up and about so early. And how he's got himself up! He's put on his best shirt. There's something rotten here.

Usually I spent the morning in the village. But on this Sunday I thought it advisable to get back to the pasture as quickly as possible. I attended a short, silent mass. Without waiting for the usual gossip with my schoolfriends or my friend Alex I hurried to the village shop, packed some loaves, maize and pasta, and a bag of salt for the animals into my rucksack and set off on my way back. Nor did I visit my father in the Mountain Museum. He knew all about everything and could have advised me. But I wanted to sort out the matter with Bettminger and Karolina by myself. Nor was there much to talk about. I had to make it clear to Bettminger who was master on the pasture. And how he had to conduct himself towards Karolina. Such were roughly my ideas as I climbed back up to the pasture as fast as my legs would carry me.

The herd was grazing along the wall behind the rusty door. No-one was minding it. At the far end of the spit of land the turf was undermined by erosion to a depth of two or three metres. If a cow had trodden on it, the overhanging earth would have broken off and the animal would have tumbled down the steep slope into the Zmuttbach. I was furious. "Karolina can't be relied on when men hang around her. She's a real Gaagla!" I drove the cattle away from the overhanging edge and went on my way. Shortly before the Kalbermatte the path made a hop over a rise in the ground. You could see the hut from there. A long wall of loose stones divided the meadow from the pasture beyond. Karolina was sitting with Bettminger in front of the cabin. He was fumbling with her bodice and she was giggling fit to be heard for miles around.

"Wha-at, you're back already?" she said, embarrassed.

"Why have you left the herd alone?" I asked accusingly.

"What harm can the animals come to? They can't get down into the valley because of the wall. And if they come this way, I'll see them, won't I?"

"You know the overhanging grass. It won't hold if a cow grazes on it. God help you if we'd lost an animal!" Bettminger whistled through his teeth. There was a mocking smile on his face.

"Keep your nose out of things that don't concern you", I told him. It was all I could think of. I went down into the cellar, unpacked my rucksack and put the food on a hanging shelf. I cut a piece of bread and cheese with the kitchen knife, ladled myself a cup of milk from a bowl, on which there floated a finger-thick layer of cream. I went into the yard. Karolina and her beau had withdrawn behind the hut. There was a small level patch there, covered in thick white clover and meadow grass, where it was comfortable to lie. I sat down on the low wall and set about my bread and cheese. Peculiar sounds were coming from behind the hut. Not the silly laughing and giggling any more. It sounded like boys wrestling. Karolina said fiercely:

"Let go! You're hurting me. D'you hear? Ouch!"

I went round the hut. Bettminger was struggling with her. He pressed her to the ground, and they rolled in the grass. Karolina was close to tears. Her wide skirt slipped up above her knees. I don't think she ever wore panties. None were ever to be seen among the washing she laid out to dry on the stones.

"Let her go!" I said to Bettminger, violently. He just grinned and kept tickling.

"Leave her alone, you swine! Do you hear?" Bettminger was a strong man, with a back as broad as a barn door. He wasn't someone to fool with, everybody knew that. He was a hothead. A schoolboy couldn't make any impression on him. He carried on with what he was doing as if I were thin air. Seized by impotent rage, I rushed to the kitchen. Next to the fireplace was a long, rusty poker. In two or three bounds I was back beside him. Bettminger was kneeling on Karolina's thighs and pinioning her arms. That was careless of him. He left his forehead exposed. As hard as I could, I brought the poker down. I hit him above the temple. The blow produced a curious, dull sound. Blood spurted from below his hairline. It ran down his cheeks as if from a gutter. With the poker in my hand I made off as fast as I could, up the slope towards the rocks. At the Schönbühl path I turned round, thinking Bettminger was close behind me. I was wrong. He wasn't following. He was still kneeling in the same spot. With bowed head he let the blood run down his cheek and through his short beard. Karolina rushed into the hut. She fetched the cardboard box in which Mother had put some old linen that had been washed clean. Karolina tore the cloth into long strips. She hunted for spider's webs on the wall. When the blood flowed less profusely, she put the spider's web on the wound and bandaged the head. Blood kept soaking through the white linen.

"Serves him right", I reassured myself. "He's no business coming here. He should leave us in peace." I wasn't quite easy in my mind, however. I was afraid he would tear me to pieces if he met me anywhere. Under no circumstances could I go down to him now. I went back to the herd, holding the poker in my hand. I knew, of course, that in a fight the poker would not be much use to me. But it calmed me to have this heavy, rusty implement.

Above the wall with the rusty door I climbed on to a ledge of rock. From there I could overlook the herd and the path. I would also see Bettminger if he tried to get to me from above. I was protected by the overhanging rock. The next ledge had an opening under it like an elongated cave. Goats and sheep, and even wild animals, liked to shelter there in bad weather. This overhanging rock had saved my father's life. When, as a boy, he went to check the sheep after thirty centimetres of snow had fallen in early summer, he found them in this place. The animals had instinctively sought shelter there. He fed them with salt from his hand. Suddenly there was pandemonium. The layer of wet snow on the steep slope gave way. An avalanche of snow and moraine thundered down the rockface. Two terrified sheep jumped from the shelter and were swept away and buried by the snow.

The rocks cast their long evening shadows towards the valley. Still there was no sign of Bettminger. I feared he was waiting at the hut for my return.

"That puts me in a difficult spot. I can't stay here. The cows have to be milked. I'll drive the herd back, but I'll keep clear of the hut," I thought. I climbed down from the ledge and rounded up the herd. The loud jangling of the cowbells, the lowing of cattle and bleating of goats must have warned Bettminger of my approach. On the rise, as I approached the hut, Karolina came towards me. She was alone, crying.

"Why did you do that?" she sobbed.

"Where is he?"

"He's gone. Didn't you see him?"

"No, he didn't come down through the valley."

"He went through the gully."

"And you didn't warn me. He wanted to get at me from below!"

"He didn't want to get at you. He said: The boy's mad. He ought to be locked up. That's what he said. And he's right. You really are mad!"

Sad eyes

Near the path to Schönbühl, on a rock, I found a sardine tin. A hiker must have had a snack there. The lid of the tin was rolled back and one fish had been removed.

Perhaps the visitor was an animal-lover who thought a bird, a mouse or a posse of ants would finish off the meal. How long the tin had been lying there I could not tell. The fish were still immersed in oil, and so had suffered from neither frostbite at night nor sunburn by day. It all looked very appetizing. I set avidly about the delicacy, fishing out each silver body in turn. I finished by drinking the oil from the tin.

After this unexpected banquet I climbed the rock with the thatch-topped pine, my thoughts fluttering cheerfully in the fresh breeze while the herd grazed nearby. I heard their bells jangling around me, and their placid browsing seemed like a confirmation of my contentment.

Cows are not stupid. They're clumsy, of course, as is unavoidable with their massive bodies. But their real trouble is that they lack any power of decision. They have no opinion of their own, unlike goats, for example. One might say that cattle are politically immature. But couldn't one say that of many human beings as well? Cows have good memories. After years of absence they can still remember the stall they once occupied and where the crib for their fodder stood. They often display a touching attachment to the people who look after them, although they don't find it easy to overcome their embarrassment and show their affection. It would ill become me, at any rate, to speak disparagingly of the intelligence of these animals. Our lead-cow Tschäggi once put mine to shame.

I should start by saying that Mother had a special way of dealing with animals. She talked to them as she did to us children. The animals understood her. In Zumsee Tschäggi kept trying to climb the stairs to the kitchen when Mother was there. She stood with her forelegs halfway up the steps, then got into difficulties. Just as well, since she would have got on to the landing otherwise. Heaven knows how I should have got her down. Naturally, Mother then came out of the kitchen with a crust of bread and some kind words.

Often all three cows would jostle for her attention. Each wanted to rub its head on her breast, lick her with a rough tongue or give some other token of ardent bovine tenderness. When I rushed up to help her, I was usually not welcomed by any of the parties.

The worst part was when we had to slaughter a cow in autumn. During the early morning feed Mother had a long talk with the victim. She never wanted to let it out of the stable to be led to the village square, where the butcher had everything laid out in readiness. Father or the butcher had to fetch the animal from the stable.

Cows have big eyes. In them you can see whether they are contented or sad. Tears often course from the lashes. Cows have eyelashes like blonde women. Altogether, they have much womanliness about them. When they look with their big, shining eyes, they show their whole trust but also a cautious fear of meeting you. They would like to come forward and snuffle at you, but have often met with blows and rebuffs rather than understanding and reciprocated feelings. They hesitate. With wide eyes they size you up: "Can I trust him? Perhaps he'll reject me." Then they say to themselves: "But one shouldn't be too mistrustful. Perhaps he's not such a bad person and I'm wrong to withhold my affection." They turn back towards the alien human being: "I know I have a dopey look, that's the way I'm made. And how he's saying: Look how that stupid cow is staring at me!"

Cows need company. They feel lonely when kept in a stable on their own. A goat or sheep means as much to them as a poodle or cat to a lonely human being. And the fondness they show for a new-born calf is touching to behold. They feel a true maternal bliss when they are allowed to keep their offspring beside them to lick.

I was frequently hard on my animals. Too often they had to endure my blows. But we also exchanged tendernesses. Then they were content. Experience taught them to take the cowherd as he was, accept his moods and show him a certain trust.

One day the Matterhorn had a peculiar pennant of cloud attached to its head. The north and west faces were cloudfree. Only the east face, between the peak and the shoulders, emitted vapour. I believed the Horn was playing this cloudy hide-and-seek, the cloud appearing to come out of itself, purely for my benefit. A conjuring trick to arouse my amazement and curiosity. Normally clouds came from somewhere and vanished on the other side of the world. This cloud seemed to come from inside the mountain. I forgot the animals standing on the steep slope gnawing the grass. The little stream that hopped giddily down the slope to water the meadows ensured good grass even during droughts. Suddenly I heard the lead-cow's bell. Like a hound that has scented prey, she was charging down the steep slope. With her tail stuck stiff in the air, she was making it clear that something extraordinary had happened to her. The other beasts were seized by the same urge. I had no choice but to climb down from the rock and chase after the animals, without knowing what was afoot. "Tschäggi must have trodden on a wasps' nest," I thought. We had wasps that lived in extended families underground.

They were especially aggressive and dangerous. The entrances to their big paper houses were always well concealed. They didn't swarm around the entrance to attract their enemies' attention. But if a person or an animal had the misfortune to pass close by and shake the nest, they shot out of the ground like bullets and attacked anything that moved. They were painful assailants with their poisoned stings.

I was once unlucky enough to lower my trousers in the immediate vicinity of such a wasps' nest. The spot was sheltered on three sides by rock walls. Nothing indicated the presence of a large colony of belligerent insects. Hardly had I unbuttoned my trousers and begun to squat when the attack was launched from a tussock of grass. Perhaps the unusual target had confused them. I took a few desperate leaps down the stony slope, beating off the creatures with both hands and leaving my trousers to their fate. They lost their last hold and slipped to my ankles, tying my legs together. That was a considerable hindrance to my escape. I fell over and injured my elbow. Thus prostrated, I finally obtained the mercy of the angry wasps. They spared me further humiliation. Perhaps they recognised me as a local resident, curbing their ire for that reason. Local inhabitants always get special treatment in the mountains.

I thought Tschäggi must likewise have fallen foul of the wasps. I ran after the herd without giving way to panic. As they neared the enclosure, they changed direction. They didn't run towards the stables, but across the path towards the rusty fence.

Only then did I notice Mother coming up the path. She was wearing her usual clothes and her headscarf. Her basket swayed on her back. She never came empty-handed. She called the animals by their names. Tschäggi behaved like a little dog. The goats couldn't understand the uproar and bleated impatiently. Only the calves looked on unmoved. I must have looked somewhat nonplussed as well, not understanding how the stupid cows could have spotted Mother before I had. Mother had finished her work at the Matterhorn cabin and come to see us on the pasture. We greeted each other warmly. But the animals pressed around her even more ardently. I had to take her basket so that she could ward them off. The cows did not want to graze any more, but followed Mother back to the hut. Slightly shamefaced, I trotted beside her.

The penknife

Year after year, the old Belle ladies came to Zermatt for the second half of August. They stayed at the Hotel Zermatterhof to be as close as possible to the church. They were devoted church-goers, and the priest enlisted their support on a number of matters.

Some people claimed to know that they were genuine countesses. They had been driven from their homeland by a revolution, they said. Why revolutionaries should want to throw such kindly countesses out of their castles none of us could understand. Least of all the priest. He knew only too well how generous they were.

The ladies had cut themselves off from their earlier lives and had renounced their titles. They professed democratic views and wanted to lead a Christian life in peace, like everyone else. It wasn't their fault that they owned a lot of property. Shortly before their departure, their kind hearts hit on the idea of giving all the schoolchildren a treat, so they invited them to come for cakes and tea, or rather cocoa, at a hotel. After the high mass the court usher broadcast the invitation from the church steps. He also had to announce that hens could henceforth be allowed to range freely, and would not have to be confined to their pens.

The covered veranda of the Alpine Museum in the garden of the Hotel Mont Cervin was chosen as the location for the treat. The wild youth of Zermatt were thought to be best accommodated there. On the Sunday afternoon in question a noisy throng of children assembled in good time on the veranda. They set about the cake and biscuits like voracious ants. The waitresses had their work cut out to keep the tables supplied with plates of cake and jugs of cocoa. The children had arrived like a swarm, and like a swarm they departed, leaving behind empty plates and cups and large puddles of cocoa on white tablecloths. Eating habits were not always very genteel among us. The hotel manager had had good reason to choose the veranda and not the restaurant for the occasion.

Surprised by the fast feeding habits of the children, the Belle ladies asked if they had really given the little people a treat. Or had a storm just struck the veranda? It had all gone so fast. When my father locked the museum and was walking home through the garden, he met the two ladies. They asked him: "Wasn't a child of yours at the party?"

"Yes, one of my lads. The other had to mind the cows on the alp."

"What, one of them couldn't come? Isn't that a pity," said the elder lady.

"Yes, it isn't right," agreed the younger. "We must pay him a visit and take him something. He shouldn't go short just because he has to work already."

We heard more details about the party from a mountain guide passing on his way to the Schönbühl cabin. He told us that the Belle ladies were to come to the Kalbermatte the next day with a present for me.

"With a present for Hannes?" Mother repeated incredulously.

"That's what they said. Because he couldn't go to the party."

"How kind of the ladies. They do so much for the church, and now they're giving presents to the schoolchildren as well."

"Well, they're no ordinary folks," said the guide mysteriously. "They used to be aristocrats!"

I wanted to know what was so special about aristocrats. "They're noblewomen like countesses, princesses or queens."

"And they want to come to the pasture?" I said. "Perhaps they'll bring me a penknife!"

"Oh, Hannes," said my mother. "They're not fairies.

They'll bring you a piece of cake to give you a treat."

"Perhaps they'll bring a penknife all the same."

"No, you can get that idea out of your head. But whatever they bring, you'll thank them nicely for it."

"I'll say merci."

"You'll talk proper German to them."

"Why proper German?"

"Because they won't understand you otherwise."

"Merci is proper German as well."

"No, merci is French. You'll tell them how glad you are that they haven't forgotten you and have come all the way up to the pasture. And then you'll thank them..."

"What, all that? And then in proper German?" I interrupted.

"Yes. I'll write it down for you. Then you can learn it by heart."

Mother found a piece of brown paper and scribbled a few sentences with a blunt pencil.

"Then you'll kiss the ladies' hands."

"Kiss their hands? Never. No, definitely not. I won't do it. I don't know how to do it either."

"I'll show you."

"No, I won't do it. When you know all the things people do with their hands..."

Mother laughed: "These people wash their hands several times a day. Not once a month like you."

I learned Mother's welcoming speech by heart. The longer I pored over it, the more I believed my words were going to make a deep impression on the two countesses. They will say: "How beautifully you said that! You are a fine, noble young man. We'll give you a castle with a moat."

But I don't want a castle. I want a penknife. One of those with a saw, scissors, a screwdriver and two blades. The shopkeeper by the Triftbach has got one in his window. It's decorated with a Swiss Cross in a gilt frame.

"Why won't they give me a penknife?"

134

"But Hannes, penknives are expensive. People can't go spending money like that!"

Next morning my mother sent me to the well with the soap and a clean shirt. She checked my hands, neck and ears before I was allowed to drive the herd into the enclosure. The path from Zmutt to the Kalbermatte passed there. And that, I thought, was the appropriate place for me to receive my present.

When the sun stood directly above the peak of the Matterhorn, I saw two women coming along the valley, accompanied by a guide.

"That's not them," I thought. "These ladies are wearing ordinary white hats. Not long red robes or other things that queens and fairies wear."

When they were near enough, the guide called to me to come down to meet them.

"Is that them after all?"

I tried to remember the sentences I had been able to rattle off so glibly the whole day, but they had deserted me. Hard as I tried, I couldn't remember a single syllable. I walked along the stream bed, embarrassed. I drove off the two calves grazing nearby with a stick, in case they disturbed the presentation. Then I stood before the ladies, who both looked at me with kindly smiles. The younger one held out her hand to me. I grabbed it and did as Mother had told me. I kissed it. Somewhat clumsily and shyly, it's true, but with the necessary sound. Then I looked at them, and as if a floodgate had opened the sentences I had learned poured from me in the resonant language of Goethe.

The ladies were visibly touched.

"You said that very nicely," said the elder lady.

"We know your father," the younger one went on. "You're very like him."

I was embarrassed. What answer was there to that? And then in proper German! Perhaps she's going to say I can wish for a penknife.

"I've brought something for you," said the elder lady.

"Something to play with. I'm sure you sometimes feel a little bit lonely up here on the pasture."

I gave a precautionary shrug so as not to endanger my present. The guide fished about in his rucksack. Then the lady passed me a box packed in fine paper with holly leaves and red berries, a box that rattled very promisingly.

"Now we're going to visit your mother and will see you again before we go down."

"Thanks," I mumbled in my agitation, the box with the fine paper and the gold string in my hands.

"Something from me as well," said the guide, pulling a juicy pear from his pocket.

When the ladies had disappeared round the next corner, I unpacked the parcel. A piece of cardboard with innumerable holes in it was spread over the middle of the box. At each side were coloured pegs that could be put into the holes to form colourful patterns. I had never played with anything like it and looked at the many holes and pegs in disappointment.

"They weren't to know I wanted a penknife," I thought to console myself.

But that still left the pear. To prolong my enjoyment, I licked the fruit. This caused the stalk to break off and the pear rolled into a marmot's burrow. The hole sloped down into the debris. No matter how I strained and wriggled, I could not get hold of the pear. It had gone too far down the burrow. I stood with hanging head. I could have cried. "Pity I haven't got a penknife. I could have cut the pear in half; then it wouldn't have fallen down that blasted hole!"

Thou shalt not...

In a corner of the shed we had converted into a cheese dairy I found a long thin chain buried in the clay floor. It was attached to something. I dug up the floor with the pick. An iron implement began to appear, a trap. It was badly rusted. Its solid construction showed that it had been built for foxes, marmots and badgers. When I loaded it, the doors with saw teeth formed a circle around the plate that triggered their fall.

Who can have used this murderous appliance? A hunter or poacher? A shepherd who caught illicit prey? Or even that unhappy man who had sheared other people's sheep and sold the booty, for which his spirit was now doing unquiet penance? It was a thrilling find.

Mother was alarmed when she discovered the trap.

"Throw that thing away! It's a heap of rust. You'll hurt yourself on it."

"I wonder whether it still works," I said. "I'll clean it. Perhaps it can still be used."

"You know that trapping is forbidden. It only torments the animals. I don't want you to do anything silly."

"I know, I know. I don't want to catch any animals. Maybe just a fox. There are some hanging about in the cave below the Titer."

"No foxes either, do you understand? They like living as much as we do. Come on, throw that junk away!"

"All right, in a minute. I just want to try it out. Does there have to be such a hurry?"

Mother pulled her coloured headscarf tighter. Two vertical lines appeared on her brow. She looked at me with her chestnut eyes, the same colour as her hair, which hung in little curly wisps over her forehead and ears. She moistened her parted, clearly outlined lips, but said nothing.

After a while her thoughts took a more cheerful turn. She showed her strong, dazzling white teeth. The two eye teeth were sharp, like those of a beast of prey. But her eyes were twinkling mischievously. "I'm thinking of the story of Biner Franz. He set a trap like that, as there was a fox prowling round his hen-run. When he went to get the eggs the next day, he had forgotten that his trap was buried near the gate. He wasn't one of the brightest. The trap promptly shut on his foot, giving it a nasty bite. The poor fellow limped for months." Mother laughed. I didn't find the story funny. The man had hurt himself on the trap, after all.

When I drove the cattle out to pasture, I took the trap with me. I rubbed the iron with a small piece of slate till the metal showed through. The hinges were very stiff. Opening and shutting the doors dozens of times did not help. I didn't have any oil. I tried butter and raw bacon. The joints got better. Soon they had a silky action. I greased the whole trap. With its many saw teeth it looked once more like the gigantic jaw of a skull. It could be very sensitively adjusted. The weight of a stone the size of a plum would set it off. The doors with the murderous teeth fell with a frightening crash.

I couldn't stop thinking about the trap. I observed the cave below the Titer more often than before. Not far from it, on warm days, I would catch sight of a fox looking for berries. I had a strong desire to place the trap near the cave entrance. Simply to put it there, not bury it. Just to see what would happen. Naturally, the trap had to be loaded and very delicately adjusted. With a scrap of bacon on the plate.

Needless to say, the fox did not accept such an obvious invitation. He left the bacon to the flies and ants and smiled a toothy smile over the stupidity of shepherds. But of course, I didn't want to catch him, just tease him a little. I had not yet noticed that the trap had long since snapped shut and that I was the one trapped inside. I carried the dangerous device around with me on the pasture every day, getting twigs and small branches to play the part of the incautious animal. I no longer answered the warning cries of the marmots, but looked on mutely as they tumbled about in front of their burrows. I was struck by how many fat, old animals there were among them who could only waddle clumsily to the feeding grounds. They could hardly get up on to their back legs, and showed yellowish brown incisors when they let out their whistle of warning. They hadn't much longer to live.

Near the boulder with the thatched tree I came across a particularly interesting warren. There was a little grassy knoll there. Holes led into the burrow from all sides. The warren was inhabited by a whole clan. The young animals played in front of the holes like little monkeys. The old ones lazed around, one eye shut, the other half open to survey the scene. It would have been a simple matter to trap these idlers. But something held me back. Not just Mother's admonitions. Something deeper. Was it the experience of last autumn?

It was a lovely autumn morning. The leaves of the trees had already changed colour. With the rifle I had purloined from my father I crept towards the wooded hill that shielded the village of Zumsee from Zermatt. Near the Zmutt stream and towards the valley the hill was covered with trees. Birdsong came from every one. I stopped behind a bushy larch and listened to the merry sound. I hoped to meet a squirrel. As I lurked behind a tree, a finch settled on a branch. If it had stayed put, it would have been shielded by some twigs. But it flew two branches higher. Puffing out its feathers, it was an ideal target.

I cautiously raised the gun and took aim. As the bird tumbled to earth through the branches like a little shuttlecock, I ran joyously to the spot. It was lying on the root of a tree. The claws of its delicate feet were still quivering. Its head was bent against its breast, the beak open. In one place the feathers stood up in a downy tuft.

I picked the bird up. Its body was warm. It lay lifelessly on my palm, losing a few drops of blood. All my joy and pride left me in an instant. I stood there with the dead bird in my hand not knowing what to do. Why had I killed this little creature? I could just as well have shot at something else.

In the wood the birdsong continued blithely. From every side came call and answer. The wind rustled in the branches. Golden needles fell from the larches, shining in the sun against the blue sky. Now and then quiet fell among the trees. Still I stood there with the dead bird in my hand. Even if Moses, the tough old trooper of the Old Testament, had not carved his wise rules in tablets of stone on Mount Sinai, I would have understood the shamefulness of my action.

The dead bird burned in my hand. I laid it under the tree and covered it with russet larch-needles. Shamefaced, I crept home with the gun. I wondered why the hunt for the animal was so full of sweet excitement, while killing it aroused such shock and disgust. I do not know what finally drove me to set the trap in front of the marmots' warren. I dug a small hollow in front of the entrance and put the trap into it, carefully covering all the metal parts with fine debris and earth. Nothing gave away the open iron jaws with their murderous teeth. The chain the led from the trap to a post was also buried. No marmot could suspect the danger that threatened before the entrance.

After two days I made a check. I could hardly believe my eyes. There was turmoil in front of the hole. The chain was in the open, and pulled tight. The upturned trap was hardly visible inside the hole. The earth was churned up all round the entrance. I took hold of the chain. At once I felt the resistance of an animal behind the trap. I dragged the trap out of the hole. A young marmot was pinned to it. One of its front legs was squashed between the saw-teeth, the bone crushed. The paw was only joined to the leg by skin. I started to panic. I tried to open the trap, but the marmot snapped at my fingers. It pulled the trap back into the hole. I looked for a piece of wood and held the trap with it while I forced the jaws open with my shoes. The teeth had hardly parted when the animal pulled out its injured paw and disappeared like lightning into the burrow.

Marmots are tough creatures. The don't like dying, as every hunter knows. So he tries to make sure he shoots the animal in the head. With a body wound every marmot will escape to its hole. It will hold in its entrails with one paw to stop them falling out and scamper to the entrance on three legs to die in peace in the burrow.

Sweat stood on my brow. I looked round to see if anyone had been watching. Not a soul was to be seen on the path to the valley or on the pasture slopes. I felt miserable. I picked up the trap in shame, hurried to a scree slope and hurled it between two big rocks.

The whole afternoon I fretted, wondering how the young animal with the crushed paw could be faring. I reproached myself for not killing it straight away to spare it the prolonged suffering.

When I reached the hut, Mother told me a Dutch couple had been there and drunk tea with her. The lady had said that when they came back to Zermatt next summer she would bring me a penknife.

"Whatever's the matter? Aren't you glad that you're going to get a penknife at last?"

"I'm not well, Mother."

"I can see that. You're quite pale. You're ill, my lad."

"I... I've got... tummy ache."

"Tummy ache? I'll make you some camomile tea. Go to bed. I'll wrap you up warm. Karolina can do the milking. Off you go."

I went inside the hut with dragging feet, wondering how I was going to tell my mother.

Alp Sunday

On the raised ground between the hut and the valley stood Bettminger. He was looking over to the other side of the valley, pretending not to notice us.

"He's come to fetch me," said Karolina, somewhat embarrassed.

"Then call him," Mother replied. "I'd like to offer him something to drink."

"No!" I interjected vehemently.

"Why not? What have you got against him?"

"They recently had an argument," Karolina explained. But she was already hailing Bettminger. He turned his head before the echo came back from the rock wall. Karolina waved to him. He came towards us.

Karolina had packed her things. The summer was over for her, as Mother was now at the pasture. For me the world had its protective glow again. Karolina had wrapped the carved frame with her picture in a blouse that had seen more than its share of use, so that it would suffer no damage in the basket. She guarded the photo of "Gaagla" like a jewel. With some tips from the sale of milk and her two months' pay of twenty-five francs each, she was more than happy to go back down to the valley.

Since that day Karolina had not said another word about Bettminger. When I saw him standing on the rise, I felt my heart thump. I had always been afraid of running into him on some remote path. He had a score to settle.

Bettminger greeted Mother, and kissed Karolina.

"Aha, so there was something between them."

Then his sombre eyes, almost hidden under the lashes, sought me. I sat a little way off on a stone, suspiciously eyeing the new arrival. He still had a plaster on his left temple.

He came up to me and fumbled in his coat pocket. "For you! Made it myself. You can keep it."

It was a watch-chain of the kind the alpine herdsmen plait from shoe-laces or thin strips of leather. I didn't have a watch, of course, but who was to know that if I had a watch-chain dangling from buttonhole to pocket? You could tie anything to it. A thin oval stone or a beer mat.

"You made it yourself?"

He nodded. "I'll show you how to do it."

He untied the knots.

"You see? Like that. Simple, isn't it? Then you knot the strips again. Finished. No-one's going to break it! Stronger than any gold chain."

"Thanks."

I was relieved. "He hasn't got a grudge against me."

That was good. It can be very awkward to meet a foe unawares in the mountains.

After Bettminger had drunk two glasses of milk, he picked up the basket. Karolina held out her hand to me. Her eyes shone a mossy green.

"You've been a good boy."

"Goodbye," I said in embarrassment.

Karolina linked arms with Bettminger and they left. On the hill before the enclosure they turned round and waved to us. Then they went down into the valley.

Autumn was drawing near. The nights grew colder. The bilberry bushes and bearberries changes colour. The rowan trees showed their first yellow leaves. The grass hardly grew any more.

From the Stafelalp came boisterous cries and the cheerful jangling of cowbells. Over there people were leaving the pasture. The farmers were fetching their animals. In big baskets they carried their bundles of cheese and butter behind the herds. All day long there was a merry hubbub on the other side of the valley. Towards evening it grew quiet. The open stable doors yawned across to us through the pine-wood.

From the Zmutt side the farmers drove their herds to another alp for late pasturage. They grazed the slopes and hollows up to the wall with the rusty door. I too drove my animals near the wall, so that they would have some friends to play with after their long isolation.

The last Sunday the herdsmen spent together on the pasture was called Alp Sunday. Usually a very merry time was had on the pasture that day.

"You can go with the other herdsmen today," said Mother. "I'll look after the herd. I've put out a clean shirt for you." To pull a freshly washed shirt over my head was a real joy. It smelt of soap, cotton and spring water. I felt well-dressed. The white stripes of the collarless blue shirt shone in the sun. I put an edelweiss flower in my buttonhole and was in the best of spirits. My trousers, too, looked like new. The ragged ends of the legs had been hemmed with ribbon, and a new knee patch hid any nudity. With a pair of rusty scissors Mother had cut my hair short over my ears.

"Now you look presentable," she joked. "But don't turn all the girls' heads!"

Bread and cheese were wrapped in an old headscarf: "There's enough for the others as well. Let them see that we're not stingy. But don't get overexcited."

Overjoyed to be spending the whole Sunday with other young herdsmen, I sauntered off down the path.

The cow-bells clanged from every side. Groups of herdsmen and girls were sitting on the grassy moraine hills. Exuberance crackled among them. The last Sunday had to be celebrated. There was not a stir in the air. The sun filled the valley with warm light, and the grass gave off a sweet, aromatic tang.

Everywhere people were talking and laughing noisily. Petschu Hermann took his accordion from his rucksack. With the first, lilting dance-tunes the festivities began. People sang the well-known songs about the "Polish

Maid" and the "Village Fair" and yodelled and danced as if the world were newly created. A big pan of black coffee bubbled over a fireplace built of rocks. Schnapps and sugar were passed round and poured into cups and beakers. Some boys were smoking their first, fateful cigarettes leading to pale faces or something worse. Food was shared out and jokes, however stupid, were enjoyed.

The more the pan bubbled, the wider billowed the skirts of the dancing girls. Shoes scratched on the hard turf. Whoops of delight went forth. Heated, merry faces beamed and chortled. And so began once more that ticklish game that has no name, to which Alp Sunday owed its notoriety. Some cheeky wag needed only to shout: "Who's got the nicest titties?" and off it went.

As if at a command, all the girls ran off. Behind the prettiest dashed the big boys. Two or three girls who already had well-formed, womanly curves were caught. With much pleasant tussling they were held fast, their bodices or other encumbrances unbuttoned or pulled off one by one, until the white little apple- or pear-shaped breasts could be admired by all around.

I too craned my neck from behind a circle of boys to catch sight of the dazzling wonders. The girls were released again. Protesting not too vehemently, they buttoned up their bodices, well aware that only the village beauties were "honoured" in this way. The wild game was not without a certain tender chivalrousness and never gave rise to complaints from parents.

But woe to us all if it came to the ears of the priest.

In that case thunderbolts would be hurled from the pulpit at high mass the next Sunday, and Alp Sunday would be likened to Sodom and Gomorrah. All those involved would be dispatched to the lowest reaches of hell, where especially scorching places awaited such miscreants. I, who had only peeped at the forbidden fruits over the boys' shoulders, awarded myself a somewhat cooler spot.

There were red faces and giggles in the pews, but what was done could not be undone. On the contrary, more than one worthy Christian secretly resolved to be there next year, where such delightfully sinful things went on.

In the late afternoon I went back to the Kalbermatte. The cattle were grazing by the rusty door. Mother was sitting behind a big rock playing a mouth organ in the evening sun. A visitor had given us the instrument. He had so enjoyed the fresh alpine milk! Mother could play a few jaunty polkas and "schottische" on it.

I sat down beside her in the grass. She put her arm round my shoulders.

"I'm glad you've come through the summer. I was very worried about you."

I shrugged my shoulders.

After a while she added:

"I should never have dreamed that I would have to tend cattle on this pasture. When I was working over at the Gasthaus Stafelalp before I was married, I often looked over at the Kalbermatte. We made fun of the tiny house. We said there wasn't even enough room for two people to make love in it," she laughed.

She did not quarrel with her fate, but moisture shone in her dark-brown eyes. In her embarrassment she picked up the mouth organ and played a little dance. As she played, she looked at me mischievously with slit eyes through her lashes. I thought:

"How lucky I am to have a happy mother!"

End of season

In the first half of September the last holiday-makers left the Matterhorn village. They were followed by a stampede of shopkeepers. As the grocers on the main street came without exception from outside the village, almost all the shops shut. Only two of these alien grocers took on themselves the rigours of the long winter. Being a shopkeeper was regarded as dishonourable. "Is it not sinful to buy goods for a franc and sell them to some poor devil for one franc fifty?" the village folk asked indignantly. The poor devils included all of them. However, the only Zermatter who ran a general store saw things differently. He was doing very well out of it. They called him "Rich-Josi". (Rich-Joseph)

When my father came back from his last expedition to the Andes with frozen limbs, the council of the "Burgers", or long-established citizens, wanted to let him have a corner of the hotel garden on the village square. He was advised to set up a souvenir shop to bring in some income for his family. He took the offer as an impertinence beyond comprehension.

"Whatever are you thinking of," he rebuked the councillors. "I'm no small-minded shopkeeper!"

The hoteliers, too, who, during the season, had sung the praises of the incomparable Matterhorn, the marvellous, healthy air, the fine weather and their beloved Zermatt, left the village in a hurry when their tills stopped ringing. With fat briefcases they made off for the lowlands in the little red train. The Seiler family, who had a dominant position in the hotel trade, left only the foreman and a carpenter behind in the village.

The hotel fronts were closed, the shutters bolted, the verandas boarded up, doorways and service entrances blocked, buses and carriages hidden in sheds. The horses were trotted back along the valley. Old Zermatt life prevailed once more in the village street: the slow tread of nailed shoes, the baskets and milk churns on bent backs. Cattle, goats and sheep jangled along the main street. The inhabitants were at home with each other again, bound toegether by the village square, the church and the four inns for the coming nine months.

Father, too, could lock up the museum. Aunt Ida helped him scrub the floor and staircase. He covered the stuffed animals with newspaper. It was supposed to protect them from dust – the chamois and ibexes that guarded the museum entrance, the eagle with stretched wings, poised for flight with a rabbit in its talons; and the fox that looked the spectator insolently in the eye while holding a blood-stained, white grouse under its paw.

The souvenirs of mountaineers were laid out in four different rooms. A slightly yellowed photo showed the victim still in full possession of his strength above a glass case containing mementoes found at the scene of the accident. Croz's rosary, Hadow's prayer book, Whymper's broken rope, Mosley's dented drinking flask, Uncle Franziskus's ice-pick, and so on. Accidents happened again and again, and the memorabilia accumulated from year to year. Father looked after them during the short summer season. He had been given this job by Alexander Seiler when he could no longer work as a mountain guide.

Father was very knowledgeable about climbing accidents. He explained them in all their details. The many visitors listened with interest, liking to talk to him about the perils of the mountains. These conversations gave rise to friendships that lasted for years and often carried over to the next generation. Through his intimate knowledge of the mountains and the course of the accidents, the victims lived on in the museum. When he shut its doors and shutters, twilight and deathly silence reigned in the rooms, until the next summer brought their resurrection. It was the era of "sacred alpinism". The mountains were looked on with reverence, experienced as a primal force of creation, a place of inwardness and self-discovery. To hike in the mountains was to be closer to heaven. Thus, a mountaineering accident shook the whole village community, local people and visitors alike.

My father now had a number of pleasurable days ahead of him. Expectantly, he took his rifle from the gun cabinet, wrapped it in an empty sack and hid it in the basket he carried on his back to the high pasture. He shared Karolina's straw bed with my mother. Though he claimed he had too little room and slept badly, he was in high spirits and looked forward to his days of hunting. He wanted to shoot a few marmots and a fox.

The hunting season was not open. From time to time cantonal gamekeepers made patrols in the area. They came unexpectedly from nowhere and disappeared over some pass or other into another valley. It was thus not without danger to stroll about the pasture with a rifle. He had to proceed with utmost caution, for the fines for poaching were very steep. On his hunting forays he constantly observed all animals, paths, gulleys and stony tracts. The slightest hint of danger turned him at once into a diligent firewood gatherer or haymaker.

"If I can't go up on the mountains any more, at least I want to do some hunting" – that was how he justified his activities. "And the official hunt has become too strenuous for me."

He had very personal views on who the game on the alps ought to belong to: to the citizens of Zermatt, of course, who had lived in the region for generations. He regarded it as presumptuous of the state to lay down rules saying when he could or could not shoot a marmot.

"Do you catch me poking my nose into the Sion councillors' affairs?"

When he had bagged two fat marmots early one morning, his hunting zeal was appeased. The same morning we took the animals down to Zermatt, along with two summer cheeses, some balls of butter, and the rifle hidden in the sack. From a long way off we saw someone coming up the path. From time to time the stranger stopped to survey the surroundings with binoculars. My father slowed his pace. Suddenly he cursed:

"Devil take it – a gamekeeper."

I wanted to throw down my basket and make off like a smuggler caught red-handed. Father advised:

"Greet the rogue politely when he reaches us. Don't give anything away. I'll do the talking, you understand?" The gamekeeper came up to us.

"You just down from the alp."

"That we are."

"Did you hear a couple of bangs today?"

"Just a couple? I could have sworn I heard three."

"Makes no odds whether it was two or three."

"It didn't sound quite like explosives going off," Father mused hypocritically.

"Of course not," retorted the gamekeeper, getting irritated.

"But the hunt's not open yet, is it? I don't understand."

"I understand all right. Someone's been poaching again. Always in this area. What you got in your baskets?"

"The summer cheese. We're coming off the pasture tomorrow."

"Aha. Mind if I take a look?"

My knees were knocking. I think I must have gone red in the face. Father said: "Of course. Take a good look at our cheeses. They didn't all turn out as I would have liked, but they're not at all bad all the same."

The gamekeeper was satisfied. You can't suspect honest folks all the time, after all.

"All right, I believe you," he said, pretending he had just wanted to test us.

He did take a look over our shoulders at the baskets from which the bald pates of the cheeses protruded, but didn't ask to rummage around in them.

"Where did the shots come from?" he asked.

"I didn't pay much attention, but if I think about it, I'd say they came from the wood over there."

"You mean the Stafelalp?"

"I'd say so," said Father.

"Aha. Just as I thought. Thanks very much."

The gamekeeper turned round and ran down to the Zmutt bridge to get over to the other side of the valley.

Father looked at me:

"What on earth is the matter with you?"

I pointed to his back.

"While you were talking to the man, blood was dripping from your basket." I felt sick. Even Father was impressed.

"Were we lucky!" he said. After a while he laughed:

"Never let them put you on the defensive. Never!" Then he told me about an experience he had had with a wild Kurdish tribe on his journey to Mount Ararat. We carried our load to the village while the gamekeeper combed the deserted woods of the Stafelalp. The following day we brought the animals and implements down to Zumsee.

Firewood and dynamite

Father was living with us again in the little house in Zumsee. We were happy to have the family together again. Only Alfons was missing; he was still working at the tunnelling site in Amsteg. I shared the pull-out bed at the foot of our parents' high double bed with Rudolf. Mother had filled the mattress with fresh straw. It was a delightful feeling to sleep on fresh straw. When you turned over, it creaked softly and mysteriously.

The animals were in the stable under the living-room-bedroom. At night you could hear them snorting as they lay down. They tugged at their chains or scratched themselves with their horns, shaking their bells as they did so. The sheep forecast a change in the weather – rain or snow – with a loud jangling. The pig grunted in its sleep. Perhaps it was dreaming of a good bite to eat, or some of the kind words Mother always had ready for it. Did the animals hear when Mother sighed in her sleep? Now and then they were so utterly quiet.

In late autumn the animals helped to warm our floor. If you stood barefoot on the boards, it felt as if we had under-floor heating. Only on cold winter days was the stone stove in the kitchen heated with root wood. It stood in the corner behind the door. The front was adorned by a relief with Christian symbols and the initials of my grandparents. You could sit on the bench beside the stove, warm your back, dry wet socks and clothes on the wooden rail above the stove and keep food warm over the hole in the top.

In the corner by the window stood the massive living-room table. At mealtimes we sat on the corner bench and the stools that surrounded the table. During the meals Father gave out instructions for our next jobs.

In autumn Father's main worry was to store enough wood for the long winter. Even my sister had to come with us to the wood and help carry the many tools, the dynamite and fuses. Trees were not allowed to be cut down. What Father looked for was healthy fallen trunks. Every stump he came to was tested to see how good the wood was and how difficult it would be to dig up and blast apart, before we set to work.

Larch trunks were especially popular with him. Their heat value was higher than that of pine. But larch roots sank deep into the earth. The heart root went straight down from the trunk and often attached itself to a rock or jammed in a split stone. Even dynamite sometimes wasn't enough. Pine stumps with their long roots just under the surface were much easier to extract.

"We'll take that one." Each time Father said this, an exciting adventure began. "First, we'll dig the soil out round the roots." They were severed with saw and axe. But suddenly we discovered a root wedged in a crack in the rock below the trunk. Then began the struggle between the exposed stump and Father with his dynamite. Often it went on all day. The trunk clung to the ground with some hidden root. Father cursed the stump, threatened it: "You've got it coming to you. Just you wait, you miserable specimen! This time we'll attack from this side." He pointed to the spot. I positioned the big hand drill and drove it 20 cm deep into the sound wood. "That's good. You can load." I fastened the detonator to a length of fuse with the pliers, pulled it through a pack of dynamite and pushed the whole thing into the hole. A short length of fuse hung out. I filled the rest of the opening with damp earth and packed it hard with the rammer.

Then came the great moment. While the autumn wind howled in the pines and the thick branches of the larches rubbed against each other and groaned, the tools were hastily placed in safety behind trees. Father sent us behind a large rock. He lit the fuse. As with a firework, little sparks hissed along the string. Father rushed to take cover with us. At once the crash came. The ground shook. Pieces of wood and stones flew through the air. The crash reverberated across the narrow valley. A pathetic wisp of bluish smoke curled up from the split stump. There was a smell of burnt gunpowder and dynamite. But the trunk had not given up the ghost. Its two halves were attached to hidden roots, which had to be dug out, hacked, sawn, drilled and loaded. The dynamite tore more pieces from the trunk until it had to surrender. The wood was piled up by a tree down by the path. As soon as enough snow had fallen, we loaded it on to sledges and took it down to the valley.

However much work the autumn days brought with them, after dinner grown-ups and children would meet by the "Flea-stone" in the village square. The old folk hunched on the logs specially put there for them, smoked their pipes and chatted about work, war and ghosts. The women, too, puffed away at their pipes. The ends of mouthpieces that had been bitten through were bound with black twine so that more burnt offerings could be made.

We children climbed about on the stone or engaged in wild sessions of hide and seek. Narrow alleys led off in all directions between houses and gardens. As soon as it grew dark and bats flitted over our heads and stars twinkled in the sky, we would creep back to the grown-ups. With the darkness, the spirits stirred from their sleep; and it was not advisable to run into them in a dark alley or a black stable or barn. Anyone who doubted this only had to listen to the stories of the old men. They had all had personal encounters with ghosts. The accounts lost themselves in elaborate detail. "You were there, too, weren't you, Hieronymus? You remember. We'd stayed late at the Gandegg cabin. We hadn't got far when it was pitch dark."

"Course I remember. I'll remember it for the rest of my days. Up to that day I had jet-black hair. The next morning my parents could hardly recognise me. It'd gone snow-white."

"We met it in front of the old house in Flescha."

"That's right. It was standing by the dung-heap between the house and the stable."

"Just where we had to go past."

"You saw it first. You were walking in front."

"You'd gone ahead earlier. But now I was in front."

"It was St. Martin's day."

"Yes, that it was. I remember it well. Old Fabian at the Gandegg cabin had warned us about going down the valley on St. Martin's night."

"That's right. We laughed at him, my word we did. But when I suddenly came up against it, I couldn't move a step. I wanted to talk to it. But you poked me in the back."

"I could hardly see my hand in front of my face, it was that dark."

"I'd have fallen over if I hadn't tried to grab hold of it."

The audience: "Jesus, you touched it?" "Unbelievable!" "And then?" "Tell us!" "What happened?"

Hieronymus took his time. He stubbed down his tobacco and drew at the pipe till it glowed visibly in the evening stillness. "We had to promise it never to breathe a mortal word to anyone."

"As long as we live, no-one will know what happened to us," Fabian concurred. "It was terrible!"

Would anyone find out any more after they were dead? The truth of such stories was not to be doubted. The encounters were described so vividly and plausibly that we children felt a cold shiver run down our backs. It seemed prudent not to dangle our legs into the darkness any more, but to sit on them. No question that the hamlet of Zumsee was a favourite haunt of ghosts. Understandable in a village whose inhabitants did not take the trouble to build a chapel! All the other villages around Zermatt had a little prayer-house, not Zumsee. We had no patron saint to drive off ghosts. So the ghosts could do as they pleased. Even the denizens of hell knew of the place, for they indulged in a few devilish pranks that would have been unthinkable anywhere else.

Once, when the priest wanted to visit his flock, his shoes pinched his feet on the stony path to Zumsee. He sat down in a meadow near the village and plucked a few plantain leaves to apply to his sore feet. When he arrived, he was surprised to find no-one coming to meet him on the village square, as was proper with such a distinguished visitor. With quick resolve he knocked at the first house he came to.

"Oh woe!" He stood horror-struck in the doorway. The devil himself was sitting at an open fire in the hearth, poking the flames with his fork:

"What are you looking for here?" the Horned One asked the holy man.

"Didn't I just see you stealing from a farmer? Give the poor people back their herbs before you set foot in this honourable house!"

The priest was thunderstruck. He even forgot to make the sign of the cross to keep the Evil One at bay. Contritely he pulled the door shut and rushed down the steps. Gleeful laughter came from the kitchen, and the wind wafted a sulphurous stink from the chimney. The priest made off at top speed for Zermatt.

Such things could not have happened if the Zumsee villagers had had their chapel. But all they have is the big stone in the village square. And how that stone came to be the centre of their hamlet is hardly to their credit. The witch of Gornera dragged it there. She really intended to do some mischief with it. But the house-high rock weighed so heavily on her bent back as she was passing Zumsee that she almost hit the ground. She dropped it in the village square.

"That's where it belongs," she is supposed to have said. "Right next to my sisters!" And she laughed out loud.

Nowadays there are no witches, of course. But old women with wicked tongues are still said to roam that neighbourhood.

The artist

We were still at table after our midday meal. Mother had cooked a cabbage dish we all liked very much. The cabbage leaves were fried dark brown in the pan, with potatoes, bacon and saveloy sausage, which was added somewhat later. It was all served as a hot-pot and was very tasty. We called it "bratuta", and there was never anything left over. There was a hammering on the front door. It sounded like someone knocking with a walking stick. It was unusual to knock. You did that with strangers or people who had something to hide, but not with neighbours.

"See who's there," said Mother.

At the door stood a bearded man. He was carrying a large rucksack and an easel on his back.

"Aha, an artist," I thought.

The wind from the valley ruffled his long, sparse hair.

The front of his head was as bald as a hen that has moulted.

"Is your mother at home?"

I ran to her. "There's an artist outside. He must want a room. But we won't take him. They've never got any money."

Mother had a weakness for artists. Everyone knew about it. Including, of course, the artists. I think they recommended our house to each other. There was always one knocking at our door. Mother could never turn them away. Probably because she knew these stubborn old birds had no money. She always found an empty corner for them in the attic. They were satisfied with a simple bed. They weren't hard to please. During the day they were out with their easels in any case. But at night they did value a roof over their heads. If there was a cup of milk, a few eggs and some bread as well, they were well content.

Mother didn't even accept a painting from them when they left, if they offered one, finding themselves short of money.

This annoyed us, as money was in short supply with us too. We also lived from hand to mouth.

Mother offered the painter the attic room, which happened to be empty. He had a petroleum cooker with him. Now and then he wanted to cook himself something hot. Mother gave him fresh eggs, potatoes, milk and bread. He asked her to write everything down. He would settle with her when his wife arrived. So we knew a second guest was to be expected.

"Perhaps she'll bring a few children with her. Then we'll have nothing to laugh about," Father complained.

Mother was unmoved: "I've let the attic room to him, and if he wants to share it with his wife, that's his affair."

The next day the painter set off with his easel. He could be seen working on the hill between the village and the valley, standing at his easel for hours. He gazed at the Matterhorn and its hilly surroundings and brushed away diligently at his canvas. In the evening he brought the painting. His eyes shone contentedly under his bushy brows.

"Have you captured the Matterhorn?" my father enquired with a mixture of irony and curiosity.

The painter showed us the canvas. We were speechless. I wanted to say something, but Mother was standing behind me and put her hand over my mouth. Father cleared his throat with embarrassment. Only Mother kept her head.

"Very pleasing, those brown tones," she said.

The painter turned to me. "You can carry it upstairs. But be careful. I need some fresh milk."

He followed me up the stairs. Then he placed the canvas against the wall and contemplated his work. He tilted his head to right and left and shielded his eyes with his hand. He was very satisfied.

"Do you like it?" he asked. "Have you heard anything about cubism yet?"

"No, only about painting. I always get an A or a B in drawing at school. In singing and gymnastics too."

"Does the picture say anything to you?"

"Say anything? No – why? Should it?"

He smiled.

"When are you going to paint the Matterhorn?" I asked.

"I'm not going to paint the Matterhorn. I let it inspire me."

"Aren't you an artist then?"

"Oh yes. I'm a pupil of Braque."

"No, you're joking. You're not a pupil any more!"

He was immersed in his painting again. I don't think he was listening to me.

"I've watched Albert Goss and Ludwig Werlen paint. They paint beautifully! You recognise everything. Every street corner. Even the people, they do them so well. I once had to fetch a beer for Werlen. He said: Painting makes you thirsty. Does it make you thirsty?"

"I don't know. I don't think so. Not more than any other work."

"Why did he say it makes you thirsty, then?"

"So you don't like my painting?" he interrupted me.

"When it's finished, I'm sure I'll like it."

"But it is finished."

I was embarrassed. "Do you call that finished? There's still room for the Matterhorn. In the big white triangle."

"That triangle is the centre of the whole work. Everything depends on it. It's the dominant. It sets the proportions and values of the planes."

I nodded sceptically and hid my concern for our guest's mental condition.

"Either he's a rank beginner or he's not quite right in the head," I thought. "At any rate, he can't paint. Our teacher would give him a straight E and show him the door."

The next day he made his solemn way to the Gorner gorge with his easel. He set the tripod up on a projecting rock on the edge of the abyss.

There he stood scrutinising the scene, making invisible brush marks now at one side of the canvas, now at the other, now at the top, now at the bottom. The raging and surging of the torrent seemed to lend him wings. At times he would stand reverently before the easel. He was either praying or dreaming. Then he grew active again.

In the late afternoon he returned with the painting. He showed it to us without being asked. Some wavy, silver-grey stripes disappeared into a colourful vortex. There was violet shadow opposite a patch of ochre, and above a bright vertical hung a kind of crescent like the outstretched wing of a bird. We exchanged glances and suppressed our smiles. Father bowed his head and hid his face with the brim of his hat.

"Hold the painting a moment," said the painter. "Do you see, that's the earth. A dark planet, heavy with its fate, caught up in the cosmic laws. The crescent puts a roof over this shadow here, and everything that's definite; everything enclosed and transient. This bright side is the spiritual. Free and open. Open to the sensuous. The dimensions vanish into this vertical. It holds everything together."

I listened with screwed-up eyes, biting my teeth together. But then I felt genuine pity for the poor man.

"He can't even paint the Gorner gorge," I thought.

"May I ask you something? What do you do with your paintings?"

"I sell them. Why?"

"Oh, I just wondered. Who to?"

"Museums or art galleries."

"What do they do with them?"

"They exhibit them."

"Aha. They don't sell them to anyone else?"

"No, of course not."

"We hang our pictures on the walls. Pictures of saints, very accurately painted. Mary, Jesus and the apostle Peter. You can recognise them all, they're so well painted."

He didn't reply, just smiled into his beard. That annoyed me. I ran to Mother.

"We're not going to get a centime out of this painter of ours. He only paints for museums."

The next day his wife arrived. She was wrapped in rags that hung to the ground. A woollen blanket was draped over her shoulders. Her head emerged through a slit in it. Her long red hair hung down her back. She wore sandals. When she walked, she floated serenely over the ruts in the village street. Father commented:

"I'd never have believed the fellow would have a wife like that."

To me she looked awful.

The new arrival was very talkative:

"You see," she told my mother, "my husband is a great artist. He's setting a completely new course. He's revolutionising painting. The newspapers are full of him, and galleries compete for his works."

Father was right, she was a madwoman. Hardly had the afternoon sun warmed the valley when the artistic lady divested herself of her trailing garments in a nearby meadow and stretched herself on the grass.

"What a shameless creature," gossiped the women of Zumsee. "She'll bring down the punishment of Sodom and Gomorrah on us. We ought to pelt her with cow pats. That's what comes of taking in riff-raff."

Mother promised to uphold righteousness. She would point out to the lady that different customs prevailed here. How exactly she was to go about it preoccupied her as she did her cooking. But it was clear to her that something had to be done.

Mother did not need to intervene. Cool, rainy days obliged the painter to harness his inspiration to more southerly climes. Now the open sea lay before him like an inkblue line, with the gold of the evening sky above it. Fringing these two expanses was a new dominant: the endlessly fleeting nothingness that museum directors and art commissions are so fond of embellishing with very material prizes and subsidies; to the painter's greater glory and their own.

Then the painter took his easel out one last time. In a sparse larch wood stood a late bloom of Turk's-cap lily with yellowing stalks and leaves. These had caught his fancy. In this last work he positively excelled himself. He lost himself in a kind of trance that was quite alien to us simple mountain folk with our nailed shoes and calloused hands. Our feet bumped against the stones too often to let us rise above earthly things and understand abstract art.

His wife was beside herself with enthusiasm: "He's having his brown-tone period," she warbled. "He'll give painting a new, epoch-making twist. Our great hour has come! He's made another breakthrough."

The Master showed his latest work. We all stuttered together. Could we laugh, or did the great artist expect our sympathy? We did not know. The canvas had countless holes in it. The holes were not all of the same kind. That was important. Some looked like little triangles, others like slits or tears. But it wasn't just the holes that made the work epoch-making, but their relation to the brown tones. They gave the work a three-dimensional plane that no previous artist had opened up. It fell to our guest to give art a new direction, and put creativity so visibly on show.

"I'm tired," said the Master. "Dividing up the surface was almost too much for me."

"I'll brew you a strong coffee," soothed his wife. "And then you can rest while I pack."

There was not much to pack. They needed only to throw a few things into a rucksack, tie it shut, and they were ready to take up their abode in another land. She carefully picked up the painting and bore it aloft to the attic.

The next day they left, not without having settled their account with Mother and tipping her for her attentive service. Mother gloated. "Who said they wouldn't pay? I've had a princely reward." We admitted defeat, but Mother had to put up with a good many more jokes about the great Master.

The Little Broken Jug

On a rubbish tip I found a fairly intact little book containing a theatrical farce for children. Some hotel guest had dropped it in the wastepaper basket and thus sent it on its magical way to me. It was a piece in Swiss dialect called "The Little Broken Jug". I read it several times, realising more and more clearly that fate had set me a task I could not shirk. An old barn, of which Father had inherited a one-sixth share, stood empty; we chose it for our performance. The barn stood on a large rock. Its four crooked wooden legs were pegged into a heavy wooden frame that had been recessed into the rock. The upper part projected beyond the lower, lending the building a certain dignity, though not everything was straight or perpendicular. Sun and weather had tinged the once rust-brown timbers mouse-grey.

Access caused us a number of problems. It is in the nature of a barn that it rests on round stone slabs lying on wooden legs. The slabs deny access to mice and other creatures. Hence, there is never a ladder or staircase leading to the entrance of a barn. People have to overcome this deliberate obstacle with a big step. For us children it meant a good deal of climbing. But that did not deter us from making careful preparations for our performance.

The threshing floor with its knee-high board walls at each side provided a base for the stage. Other boards served as seats for the audience. After all, we owed our public a degree of comfort. My younger brother, cousin Leo, a neighbour's daughter and I were the actors, all diligently learning our lines from the same book.

We knew that for a good theatrical performance five things were needed. First, each actor must know when to come on and when to go off. Second, the parts must be said without stuttering. Third, the props must be in place before the performance. An actor must not have to notice at the last minute that the little jug he needs is not present. Fourth, someone must operate the curtain, raising it and lowering it at the right moment. Fifth, if these four rules are observed, nothing can go wrong. Oh, can't it go wrong?

The action took place in a room. That did not prevent me from painting a forest landscape on the back wall of the stage, which we had covered with cardboard. This used up all Leo's watercolours, but a good stage backdrop had to show a forest. A theatre without a forest landscape was inconceivable. The fact that the action took place in a living-room was incidental. Mother sewed us a colourful curtain from left-over pieces of cloth, so that the stage was separated from the auditorium. The only light that reached the stage was daylight, coming across the threshing floor from the open door.

A few posters on cellar doors and telegraph poles drew Zermatt's attention to the forthcoming attraction. Now, nothing could go wrong. Everything had been thought of. And indeed, on the appointed Sunday afternoon, directly after Vespers, a throng of schoolchildren made their way up to Zumsee. Full of curiosity, the young visitors climbed to the barn entrance, duly paid their admission charge of 10 centimes, sat down on the boards of the threshing floor and waited excitedly for what was about to happen. With all tickets sold, Rudolf pulled up the curtain and the performance could begin.

We almost got through it unscathed. But the theatre is a capricious world. You normally know how a play will start, but not how it will end. In a little hamlet like Zumsee the supply of acting talent was limited. My brother had to play two parts. This did not cause any difficulties at the rehearsals. The characters he had to portray were very different, but neither had to say very much. First he appeared as a gardener with a magnificent beard that we had made from the moss on an old pine. After his exit he had to come straight back on as a maid in

166

a white apron and bonnet. He had precious little time to change. He hastily exchanged the green gardener's smock for the women's dress. But when he re-appeared on stage, he still had the beard. In his eagerness he had forgotten to remove it.

He got the applause you would expect. The children would not stop laughing. It took considerable time before we had calmed them down and were able to continue with their undivided attention.

This incident contributed not a little to the audience's satisfaction with what they had seen. No-one asked for their money back, which meant something. The children were still laughing as they jumped down from the barn into the meadow and made their way home, while we counted the day's takings. All of two francs eighty were to be found in the dented aluminium cup that served as our till.

Such a lot of money had to be spent judiciously. On that we were agreed. Leo had the idea of buying our parents tobacco with it. The thought of giving them a treat with our theatre income filled us all with pride.

The same afternoon we hurried to Zermatt and bought some coarse-cut Valais tobacco. It was a particularly pungent sort very popular with the old folk.

That evening all the old men of Zumsee sat on the logs next to the Flea-stone drawing avidly on their pipes, and for once having a good word to say about the degenerate young.

Home butchering

In the evening the women of Aroleid went to the village square, puffed their pipes like the men, kept their hands in their laps and gossiped.

My mother did not smoke. After the evening meal she had trousers to patch, socks to darn or shirts to wash. She was the first on her feet in the morning. She tended the animals before daybreak. You could hear her talking to the cows, goats or pigs in the stable below. The barn was about sixty metres to the west of the house. She fetched hay for feeding, brought water for the drinking troughs in a big can from the village well, and forked the dung from the stable. Outside the snow often lay metres deep, and a biting cold cut into one's face. In the winter months she always performed these tasks in darkness.

In the kitchen the burning wood crackled. The stone stove in the living room was fed from the kitchen. Often the water in the storage containers was frozen to blocks of ice. She had to throw them into the snow in front of the house and fetch fresh water from the well. We, meanwhile, were still in bed. Father slept especially soundly and long. Half-awake, I heard Mother busy at the stove, boiling the milk for breakfast, sometimes singing a little refrain: "In Lauterbach my stocking I lost". She might also play the mouth organ or dance a schottische in her wooden shoes to warm herself. She was always cheerful. While she cooked, she often took me in her arms and tried to teach me the waltz. I only saw her really sad in autumn, when some of our animals had to be slaughtered to replenish our meat stocks for the winter. Then she could be quite touchy.

For us children the butchering meant an exciting and disturbing day. Our job was to boil the water on a large cast- iron stove behind the house, which was used during the year to prepare the pig swill. First the pig was slaughtered. A neighbour who knew something about butchery was hired for the day. The white apron he wore entitled him to kill and cut open pigs and shoot cows.

All the people from the village were assembled around the Flea-stone in the village square. They wanted to look on and, if needed, lend a hand. The sudden bright light and the many people in the village square naturally upset the animals. They didn't always keep still as they should as the man in the white apron raised his arm to strike. This made the victims' protests all the more vociferous. A second blow was not so easy to aim. However, it usually went off smoothly. The animal was pierced in a stunned condition, the blood caught in a bowl, while being stirred with a wooden spoon. We children filled the wooden trough with hot water and added the necessary resin. When the animal had finished bleeding, it was put in the trough to scour, and turned back and forth with chains. We were allowed to scrape off the bristles until the pig was as smooth as a man's bald head.

Once, however, the butcher was unlucky. Or, to be more exact, a pig was hounded to an unworthy end. It was the very pig my mother had had such long conversations with. It would't keep its head still. The butcher hit it on the cheek instead of between the ears, and pandemonium was let loose. The pig not only screamed at the top of its voice, it struggled desperately. It got away from our neighbour, who was holding it by a rope tied to its back leg. That was not a common occurrence. The frightened animal had to be caught. All those present, naturally including us children, joined in the hunt. Not out of pity or horror, no – with laughter and boisterous shrieks, as if it were an exciting game. When the pig finally lay scouring in the trough, I ran to the kitchen to fetch a ladle to scrape the bristles and to tell Mother about the incident. Her face was bathed in tears, because she had heard the uproar. "How can you be so heartless", she rebuked me. "You seem to be enjoying it.

You ought to be ashamed of yourself. You fed and looked after the poor creature. What kind of people are you? You can't even kill an animal with kindness!" Contritely, I took the ladle and disappeared. I heard Mother still scolding as I went down the stairs. For her, home butchering day did not hold the tingle of excitement it did for us.

Rotzipapa

It was an unlucky day. Everything went wrong. And in the evening I came home with a broken writing-slate. Father shook me by the hair and held forth on how much a new slate would cost. And all because of the accursed snow.

The valley was swathed in dark clouds. From Findeln came a whirling, skittish wind, the Rovel. Big snowflakes had fallen incessantly for two days and nights. The snow in front of the house was as deep as a man was tall. Narrow paths like open mole burrows led to the houses. On such days Mother had to light the petroleum lamp by early afternoon.

The path down to Zermatt was difficult and menaced by avalanches. We got to school late, to the great annoyance of the teacher. The whirling snowflakes had found their way into our satchels. The homework on the slates was smudged, which earned us ruler-raps on the fingers and extra work.

But that was just the beginning. Lina had hidden the rucksack with the milk bottle and the bread on a stack of logs in front of our house. By midday the milk was frozen solid, the bottle shattered. We had to thaw the milk with a petrol heater in our Zermatt flat. You could see your breath in the empty house. On the way to afternoon school we had a snowball fight. Some boys tried to hit the bulb of a street-lamp. Naturally, I tried too. It was just one of those bad days. Melanie from the Hof quarter had looked out of the window and seen everything. "Let's just hope she doesn't tell the teacher. That would mean all kinds of trouble. And Father would give us a second dose."

The whole village groaned under the mass of snow. During break-time, the men stood in front of the school-house in the pale sun. With their hands deep in their trouser pockets, they made fun of the children scuffling in the snow.

I don't know what led to my disagreement with Rotzipapa's son. We gave each other a regular pasting. When the bell rang for the end of break, my ears were crimson and my scalp hurt. I hadn't noticed Rotzipapa standing around with the men. Suspecting nothing, I ran up the outside staircase to the door. Suddenly, caught by a resounding whack, I was hurled to the ground. The blow had spun me round on my axis. Rotzipapa stood before me. He clearly felt that his offspring had taken too much punishment and that he had to redress the balance. Satisfied with his work, he turned round and was about to go down the steps. Lying on the ground, I kicked him as hard as I could with my nailed shoe behind the knee. The knee buckled. Rotzipapa slipped on the icy stair and tobogganed down the steps. A loud, gloating laugh came from the men. But I retreated as fast as I could into the school. Luckily, he did not follow me.

However, in dictation I only got a C. And when all four classes were standing around the teacher, singing "Walking is the miller's joy", I got one over the head with the teacher's violin bow. "Pay attention, you scatterbrain." The whole time I was planning how to get out of the school without falling foul of Rotzipapa. Everywhere I saw hiding places where he could be lurking. Below the bottom staircase, behind the big entrance door, behind Fabian's wood pile, and, of course, beside the hut by the Triftbach bridge.

I volunteered to clean the blackboard. That gave me time to wait till the schoolroom had emptied. The teacher was in a hurry, so that he wouldn't miss the girls' teacher in the corridor. Naturally, he had purely pedagogical reasons for this, wanting to exchange impressions of the day with her. I resolved on an audacious plan. When no-one was left in the big schoolroom, where the first four classes were taught by the same teacher, I jumped from the second-floor window into the deep snow in the priest's garden. My chin came down hard on my knees and I bit my tongue. In the course of this manoeuvre my slate was reduced to shards.

As I learned the next day, Rotzipapa had waited by the Triftbach bridge and in his eagerness had almost knocked down the wrong boy. I had chosen the route via the churchyard bridge, behind the houses and stables, to the upper village, a plan which spared me a number of hefty blows. When I got home, I had no slate to do my homework on. There was no writing paper to be found. I tore a page from my copybook to do my sums and write out a Bible text by the light of the petroleum lamp. Our teacher thought Bible texts especially suited as punishments for pupils. At the end of the story of the raising of Lazarus I wrote "Alleluia! Alleluia!", which the teacher also took amiss. I tried to show him how happy I was about the resurrection of Lazarus, not about finishing my punishment. That he would not accept.

What was worse, I had not done all the sums. Mother had served the soup early. "Hurry, the musicians are coming today." It was no use complaining that I still had to finish my sums. Father played in a Ländler band. He wanted to practise with his friends, as they were invited to play at a roofing ceremony. Even the great masters can't manage entirely without practice. So twice or three times a year the band were our guests. Moritz, another Hof resident, played the clarinette wonderfully, Isidor played the accordion and my father the trombone. Sometimes there was a dulcimer as well. They didn't play from scores. Those were superfluous. Only self-important people or those without a musical ear needed written music. Hof-Moritz started a dance on his clarinette and the rest just followed.

To make room for the musicians at table, we were sent to bed. There we were in no-one's way. The musicians played with spirit, with passion. Even the stiff-legged beds, from which we listened, in, as it were, the front row, could hardly keep their feet still on the uneven floor. We eagerly followed the polkas, schottisches, mazurkas and waltzes until sleep took us in its arms, while next to our beds the instruments screeched and the boots stamped the rhythm.

The horned sledge

"Nowadays people don't even believe in ghosts," old Rosalia complained. "What are we supposed to believe in? Doomsday?"

My mother comforted her: "There'll always be ghosts. It's just that people have no morality any more. Don't fret over it." She put a piece of root-wood into the stove. The burning wood shed a reddish glow over her hands and face. Rosalia had come into our kitchen with an empty can. Her cow had cut its hind leg during watering. She wanted to wash out the wound with fresh boy's urine. "You've got enough boys to supply me with the stuff," she said. Rudolf and I had to pass water into the tin can. We were flattered to have "healing" water.

Rosalia was warming to her theme: "I heard Christ-Josi said he just got torn old rags from that miser Philomena. Not even a beggar would have put on such tatters. So he wondered what old Philomena can have done with her dead husband's better clothes. Just imagine what the rascal did, Barbara! He went all over the village telling people they could see dead Nazi's soul in the Vehgasse at night. He said Nazi was dressed in terrible old rags. You could hear him wailing desperately: 'No-one does a good work for me, no-one!' Of course, word of poor Nazi's distress got back to the stingy widow. What else could she do but give Josi her husband's Sunday suit and his two good shirts? What do you say to that, Barbara? To misuse our faith in such a way!"

Mother laughed heartily. "The main thing is it helped the ghost."

"But you can't use a poor soul to swindle people like that. What are we supposed to believe in now? No-one knows whether the ghost really appeared or not." Rosalia looked so helpless that Mother could not help laughing again.

From outside shoes could be heard crunching on hard snow. It was bitterly cold. Father came up the stairs. His steps sounded tired. Rosalia remembered her injured cow in her shed. She thanked us for the kindness, waved the tin about and spilt some of its valuable contents on her apron before she left.

"What did the old dear want?" asked Father.

"Her cow has injured its leg," Mother answered. Father sat down by the kitchen table.

"The day after tomorrow we're going down to the village," he said. "Everything's ready. What little hay we still have left we can feed to the cattle in spring. I don't want to start December here. And if any more snow comes down, the avalanches will cut the path."

For us children these were words of deliverance. An Open Sesame. No more long trek to school. Something hot to eat each midday. Good beds with feather mattresses. And electric light to do our homework by. We could hardly wait. But more snow came down. Early next morning Father got the horned sledge from the cellar. A sledge for towing with rails that formed hoops at the front and continued in prongs like two horns. They were what you pulled it by. Mother had got ready the household equipment, and supplies of butter and cheese. And a cardboard box full of Sunday clothes. My youngest brother, who was now able to sit up, was wrapped up warmly. Father loaded everything carefully onto the horned sledge. On top came the bed linen in which the baby was wrapped. Father tied it all to the sledge with a rope. The baby too was held by the rope, without being squashed. Rudolf, who could already look after himself, was allowed to sit on the sledge. Then Father set off with the load down the steep, snow-covered path to Zermatt.

When I was small, I was allowed to ride on the sledge. It was a splendid feeling to glide past the fence-posts with their caps of snow. In the woods the snow was shaken from the branches as Father controlled the sledge with powerful movements, turning a corner without losing much speed. In particular, the stretch down to the Zmuttbach bridge was not without danger. But if anyone loved danger, it was Father. He enjoyed it most when the snow flew up in clouds. After the bridge he had to get down and pull the sledge for a while, till it went downhill again.

Mother, Lina and I loaded what was left behind into our baskets. The animals were brought out of the stable and led by their chains. They trudged unwillingly along the narrow path in the deep snow. It was a biting cold. Comic snowy beards formed on the eyelashes and nostrils of the cows. It was a silent journey down to the valley through a dead, icy world. The snow blinded the animals. The cows looked uncomprehendingly ahead. The goats bleated continuously and now and then nibbled the snow. Only the hens, which were carried in the basket, seemed content. Luckily, we reached the valley without incident.

As we arrived snow-spattered at the upper village, the bells rang for midday. Fresh snow lay on every wire, twig and branch. I felt so solemn, the bells might have been sounding to welcome us.

Winter

The previous evening there had been a disagreement at the Café Central. In the course of it, some windows had been smashed to smithereens. Father took his glazing-tools to repair the damage. The waitress claimed the belligerent parties had only come to blows so that they could sit down together afterwards and carry on drinking.

They were peaceable folk at bottom, the inhabitants of Zermatt. No-one ever tried to take anyone else's life. No chronicle, no legal records nor even the old people could report a murder among the villagers. If there were differences that couldn't be ironed out with words, they were settled by muscle. Then there was peace and order again. Neither the policeman nor the frontier guard stayed in the village over the winter. Never was any church or house door locked. To fence in a garden would have been an insult to one's neighbour, even if the precaution was only meant for the hens.

There was a thick blanket of snow in the valley. On the paths through the woods the snow had been flattened. On my free afternoon I had to accompany my father to the Aroleid wood to fetch the firewood that was waiting there. Father had stacked it in the autumn under a larch near the path. He spent much time carefully loading the split logs and roots onto his horned sledge and securing them with ropes. I was allowed to ride on the sledge on the journey down the valley. When the path ran down steeply through the wood, he tied a knotty chunk of root to the end of a rope and let it drag as a brake behind the sledge. All the same, the load took us down the mountain at alarming speed, and Father needed the help of all the saints and departed to master the dangerous corner before the ravine. When we had put the steep section behind us, his narrowed eyes gleamed impudently. "I already saw us in the gulley with the sledge," he said. Sometimes the path went uphill for a short distance. Then I had to get down from the wood and shove with all my might.

A man who prepared firewood with the help of his children, who sawed, split and stacked it, shovelled the snow from the roof when it became too great a burden on the house, and now and then fetched down some hay from an alp or pasture was counted quite a model husband. So my father sometimes had time on his hands. He stood with colleagues in the sun, warmed his hands in his trouser pockets and cracked his jokes. If the money bag was not completely empty, he might take an occasional seat in the Café du Pont and drink a schnapps. Only the shepherds had to worry about their animals every day. Cattle, goats and pigs were fed by the women. My mother always went to the stable, which was situated outside the village, when it was still dark. There was often fresh snow metre-deep on the road, which no-one had yet trodden down. So she pulled an old pair of my father's trousers over her skirt and waded bravely through the winter night.

She was back in good time in the kitchen, woke us, prepared breakfast and sent us off to school, which started at eight o'clock. When Father woke, she served him a cup of black coffee in bed, with a dash of red wine or kirsch, which did much for his mood.

At intervals the church-bells summoned the faithful to morning mass, the Ave Maria, vespers, rosary prayers, matins, the Stations of the Cross, and all the other pious rituals of the winter calendar. The only variation was carnival time, when there was uninterrupted dancing for two days and nights. Well-dressed couples walked whooping down the village street to the unheated ballroom of the Pension des Alpes. She in the pretty traditional costume or a fashionable dress she had made herself, with a hairdo worked on by a sister or aunt; he in his good Sunday suit, with a smart little barrel of wine in his hand, as everyone had to provide themselves and their friends with their own refreshments and entertainment. Only the ländler music, with my father blowing raptly on his trombone and beating time for the melodies of clarinette, accordion and dulcimer, was laid on by the dancing master.

Winter life was shaped by the snow and the weather. Enclosed by the mountains, which were petrified in icy stillness, we gave ourselves up to the forces of nature. Like our forefathers before us, we had to endure the long, hard winter season. Everyone lived on their stocks of potatoes and cabbage in the cellar, the salted, dried meat in the storehouses, the beans and pulses in the attic. The domestic animals provided us with milk, butter, cheese and cooking fat. A family would have fifty or sixty loaves of rye bread made at the baker's. They were placed on the attic floor, along the walls. In a short while they were hard and dry. Now they could not be consumed too greedily. The post sledge went daily to Sankt Niklaus carrying back letters, newspapers and the few parcels that came. At times the valley road was buried by avalanches. Then people waited patiently until the sledge got through again, bringing news from the "outside world". Occasionally a commercial traveller would stray into the village, hawking his little case of cloth patterns from door to door. We children ran after him, as such a visitor was a rarity.

When spring finally came, a green slope seemed to us like a miracle. We went looking for budding dandelion leaves for the first salad, marvelled at the crocus cups, liverwort and soldanella, and played marbles heatedly with our schoolfellows on a tiny patch of cleared ground.

Our teacher, too, scented the arrival of spring. All pupils had to present themselves at the schoolhouse with a scrubbing brush, soap, a splinter of glass and their mother's bucket. The wooden school benches were to be given a thorough wash. Amid much uproar we carried the battered benches down into the playground.

Each of us sought a place near the Triftbach. Some especially bold spirits put one leg of their benches directly in the water. All afternoon the wash went on noisily and merrily. It was amazing how pristine clean the bare, untreated wood became. Many a bench looked as if it were fashioned of ivory. Admittedly, others had been so maltreated that even a sliver of glass was not enough to scrape all the ink-stains from the wood. When school ended, we made our way home, tired but cheerful.

At the village well, near the old Konsum store, we met old Christine. The way she wore her headscarf and flailed with her arms told us she had had a glass too many. A woman whose legs refused to obey her was not an everyday sight. We jeered at her. She came up to us, laughing:

"You're just a bunch of small fry. That's what you are. No good for anything. None of you will ever be a match for me."

"Not a match for you, Christine? Well, I drank a whole litre of blueberry wine and I was steadier on my legs than you are now," boasted Karl.

"Useless little tup. You should take my example. And Bärenfeller's. There's a man for you! All I need to do is lift my skirt, show him my backside – and I get wine by the bucket. And what wine! I tell you, the fine ladies in the hotels never get served wine like that. But what do you know about it? You're just billy goats. That's what you are. No good for anything. So now you know." And she laughed at her own ribaldry. She turned on her heel, almost lost her balance and tottered towards the bridge, attempting a rendition of a little ditty: "Youth's the season made for joys." We jeered a bit more and threw snowballs after her. Arthur said thoughtfully: "Old Bärenfeller's ninety-four. D'you think he still grabs Christine's backside?"

"He's capable of anything," declared Anselm.

"If he died tonight, the devil would have him before he was in the ground."

In earlier times old Bärenfeller had run a small pub. It was a cellar with a tiny window. When his wife died, he gave up being a landlord. He usually sat on a stool in the sun, keeping boredom at bay by gossiping with the passers-by. He had put aside a modest reserve of wine for his own use. Old Christine seemed to have got wind of this nectar.

At supper I told my family of the state we had found Christine in.

"She talked some rubbish about old Bärenfeller. We teased her and tossed snowballs after her."

Father, too, had a droll story to tell about her, and we all laughed, except Mother. She didn't find it funny and rebuked us roundly.

"I'd be ashamed to make fun of a drunken woman."

"You women can only laugh about men," Father retorted. "Women always stick together."

"And we need to. Otherwise we'd be even more downtrodden."

Father laughed: "You downtrodden? You're always on top!"

"I wouldn't say that so loud," said Mother, laughing too.

But Father was right: Mother always sided with the women when there were squabbles among the neighbours. She could get quite forthright about it. "Well, what good can we poor women ever expect from life?" she once asked.

"If we happen not to be in mourning for once in our lives, if no distant relative has passed away recently, we can put on a white scarf or a coloured headscarf. That's happiness for us! Otherwise we run around for the whole of our lives in a black shawl, a timeless bodice and a boring wide skirt. Bringing children into the world and being everyone's servant – that's our lot."

"We can't be courting you all the time," joked our neighbour Peterjosi.

"Courting us? You only do that till we've swallowed the bait. Until we're married, yes, you take us out a couple of times. Maybe a walk along some path that's just been cleared in spring. Maybe even to an inn in Aroleid or Findeln, or where no-one's going to see you. You sit with us in a bower in the sun and you still have something to say to us. But once we're married – goodness me!"

"When my wife was young and we hadn't any children, I danced with her in the 'Café des Alpes' for a whole carnival. Two whole days and nights on the trot! And she still hadn't had enough. What more can a man do?"

"Walk with her through the village again."

Peterjosi thought he had misheard.

"Walk through the village?" he laughed.

"Yes," my mother replied, "simply walk with her through the village and stop at the store to buy her some little trifle. Something she doesn't absolutely need."

"Did you hear that, Franz? I'm supposed to go walking through the village with my old lady." The men laughed heartily at such an impossible suggestion. "And then I'm supposed to buy her two pennyworth of liquorice!"

Peterjosi could hardly utter the words for mirth.

Most husbands believed it to be beneath their dignity to walk with their spouses in the village. If a husband did happen to forget he was a man and took his wife's arm, his colleagues would call to him: "That's right, you hang on tight, Hans Grägu! Otherwise she might run away from you." And all the fellows standing around beside the road with their hands in their pockets would roar with laughter. Even on Sundays spouses went separately to church.

It was lucky there was a church to summon the women to countless services. There they met their friends, exchanged a few words and sighs and found out that they weren't alone in the fate they had to bear. That did give a certain comfort. Hardly surprising that the women clung desperately to the afterlife. There they were promised an existence worthy of human beings, free of earthly woe; there they would taste the angelic joy of eternal adoration. So it was worth practising patience and modesty in the meantime.

Musical box

When I came home from school, Mother was standing in front of the mirror. She was putting on her black woollen scarf.

"Hannes the Fiddler has died. You must come with me to pay our respects," she said.

In a village where several families lived in the same wooden building and the balconies of houses almost touched, children were early acquainted with death. I had looked on as old Sigrist was laid in his coffin on the first-floor balcony of our house. After that I always gave the spot a wide berth. No, I wasn't paying any respects.

"I would have liked to spare you the visit, but Johannes has left you something."

"Left me something? What does that mean?"

"You see, he knew he was going to die soon. He couldn't take his things with him. And as he has no children of his own, he gave everything away."

"He's given it all to me?"

"No, of course not. He gave something to all the people he liked. He's written it all down in a letter."

"Why does he want to give me something?"

"Because you're called Hannes, like him."

I was prepared to go with her. I was wondering what Hannes the Fiddler had left me.

He had died a bachelor. He had lived in peace with his neighbours. He expressed his moods on his violin, on which he also played jaunty folk tunes. He had been a lonely man.

Mother and I climbed the wooden stair to the first floor of his little apartment. The hall was not lit. Mother trod carefully in the dark. A glimmer of light came between the bottom of the living-room door and the worn threshold and faded across the floor. From behind the door came the pious mumbling of people at prayer, like a wailing in various pitches and keys. I held on to a fold of Mother's skirt. She quietly opened the door of the room. A musty smell met us. In the corner, on a high, rough-hewn bed, lay the corpse.

Mother walked between the chairs, on which neighbours sat, up to the dead man. He lay under a crocheted white blanket. You could see the clothes he was wearing. His black shoes poked out below the blanket. He had been prepared for the long journey. A candle flickered on a little night table. Next to it stood a glass of holy water and a crucifix. Mother took the sprig of juniper from the holy water and sprinkled the body, making the sign of the cross over him. Then she pressed the twig into my hand.

"Say: I bless thee in the name of the Father, the Son and the Holy Ghost, amen."

I did as I was commanded, but first dipped the sprig back into the glass and sprayed the body with some energetic signs of the cross. The mourners near the bed also got the benefit of my wet blessing. With the sprig in my hand, I stood staring at the crocheted blanket, which moulded exactly the shape of the body.

One of Hannes the Fiddler's female cousins came and asked:

"Would you like to see him, Barbara?"

It would have been impolite to say no. Mother knew that the sight would make a deep impression on me. She took my hand. The woman went up to the bed. Cautiously, as if afraid of waking him, she drew back the blanket to uncover the head and the hands, folded across the breast. The pale, bony face of the dead man lay on a white pillow. The candle flickered nervously, and a shadow danced on the wall. Mother said:

"How peacefully he sleeps."

The woman nodded and wept. She covered the deceased up again.

186

More unnerving to me than the body was the bed. It had a massive old frame that was no longer on an even keel. Maybe it had never been at the proper angle. But for centuries it had done service. In this bed Hannes the Fiddler's mother had brought him into the world. His grandparents had spent their nights in it. Now it was free again.

"Not for me, I hope. I don't want it."

I was depressed just looking at it. But apart from a few pictures of saints on the walls I could see nothing he might have given to me.

Mother pulled my collar straight. I turned round and said loudly: "I'm not having that bed!"

Mother was horrified. With a violent movement of her head she ordered me to be quiet. She gave me a really angry look. Then she looked at the people sitting nearest to see if they had heard me over the mumbling in the room. She pulled me by the arm to the chairs. We sat down and began to mutter a few rosaries with the other mourners. From time to time new visitors came, others went. Wet crosses were zealously sketched above the body. Sometimes he was uncovered again, gazed at in wonder and covered up. The prayers rolled on without interruption like an eternal humming. They rose to heaven in every key to be credited to Hannes the Fiddler in some fat book in the sky.

At last, Mother got up. We first went back to the bed to take our leave of the dead man with a blessing. Then Mother whispered with the cousin at the door. She told us the deceased had left me his musical box. Mother pretended to be surprised.

"Thank God it's not the bed!" I thought.

We were taken to the kitchen. The official prayer leaders, an elderly couple, were sitting at the table. A strong aroma of coffee and schnapps rose from their glasses. They needed not only payment, but stimulus to perform their pious duties. When the last of the neighbours withdrew, they had to take over the vigil and continue the prayers. In the morning more villagers arrived to release them. The prayer leaders had time to have a snack and wet their throats. That went on until the deceased was ready to be put into the coffin and handed over to the church for the Requiem mass and the burial.

In the churchyard the dead man at last found the peace he deserved. It will always be a mystery to us how this incessant mumbling could help the deceased to find eternal rest. The old custom has since been largely abandoned. But the mystery of the peace of the dead remains.

With an auspicious glance at me, the cousin went to the cupboard. When she came back, she was smiling, with the musical box in her hand playing "Be ever honest, ever true". With wide eyes and bated breath I listened to the miraculous device. Then I was allowed to receive my heirloom. We thanked the lady and left the house of mourning. All the way home we were accompanied by the dainty tones of the musical box. Mother warned me several times to take good care of it. She knew the short life expectancy of such a delicate toy in our house.

The cleansing of the temple

Hannes the Fiddler's funeral had a sequel. The priest demanded that all schoolboys should learn to serve at mass. It was a part of religious instruction.

We took turns running about on the chancel carpet in white smocks and ankle length skirts, below which protruded our hobnailed shoes. With long strides and swaying bodies we accompanied the priest to the altar, carried the large missal from one side to the other, endeavouring to kneel down and get up without treading on our skirts. We fetched the little jugs of wine and water from the side table and poured measured doses into the chalice held by the priest. If we were annoyed with him, we economised on the wine. During the sacramental act we struck the bells with all our might or swung the censer so high that the embers blazed and the nave was shrouded in smoke. At the end of the mass we walked as reverently as we could to the sacristy, not without a clandestine grin to our colleagues in the nave.

Mass was celebrated in Latin. We learned the preparatory prayers and all the sequences of pious responses till they bubbled from us like a fountain. The German text was printed next to the Latin in our prayer books, but I never made any effort to find out what it was I was gabbling. It was enough for me to recite all the celestial formulae and never miss my cue in the exchanges with the priest. Why should I bother to be an expert in these Latin prayers on top of that? The Lord understood what I was saying, and that was all that mattered.

After all, I was trying to talk to Him in His language, the one He had agreed on with His representative.

I never thought of the sacrifice of the mass as a real sacrifice, leaving aside the torture of long kneeling. All the same, I was impressed by the varied proceedings at the altar, the oriental robes, the eastern ceremony and the sonorous Latin chanting. When the church choir sent a four-part crescendo up to heaven at the top of their voices, I too felt myself borne aloft to the vault of the church. I did not doubt for a moment that our holy doings would oblige the Creator to turn a benevolent face towards us and take good note of our worries and needs. What difference did a little urchin of an altar-boy make who happened to be using a foreign language? Or who gave a prayer a somewhat alien meaning? "Sed libera nos a malo" (but deliver us from evil) sounded to me like "Setscht lieber Nusse mahlu", meaning "you'd do better to grind nuts," the wisdom of which I did not presume to question, since we longed for a few nuts with all our hearts.

When Hannes the Fiddler was buried, it was my turn to serve at mass. That was a stroke of luck. First, I could thank the deceased for the musical box from the closest possible vantage point, and then I could expect the reward of fifty centimes that was due to altar boys when someone was buried.

But when I got to the sacristy, there were already two altar-boys ready to serve. They had pulled the black skirts and white blouses with black collars over their clothes and were waiting for the priest. There followed a heated argument as to whose turn it was, but out differences could not be resolved. The argument degenerated into a scuffle. I literally tore the ecclesiastical garb from my schoolmate Hermann's back. This involved hitting to the floor and spared neither our ears, our hair, nor the holy requisites. The long tear under the armhole of the smock bore witness to the vigour of the struggle.

Hermann went back to the schoolhouse in tears and reported my un-Christian behaviour to the teacher, while I prepared myself for my pious duties. The funeral bell was already summoning the faithful.

After the Requiem I carried the long-handled cross with the castsilver Christ at the head of the procession. We had not yet left the church when I saw the furious look on the teacher's face. It boded no good.

At the grave, as the bearers slid the coffin into the ground with two ropes and the priest threw the frozen clods of earth on top of it, I again met the teacher's gaze, which had not altered in the meantime.

It was thus with mixed feelings that I entered the schoolroom after the funeral and went to my place. The teacher was clearly resolved to deal with the matter forthwith. He ordered me to stand up. He gave me his views on my sacrilegious behaviour in the consecrated house of God. "If blood had been spilt or even if a nose had been caused to bleed, the parish of Zermatt would have had to ask the Reverend Lord of Sion to reconsecrate our desecrated church!"

That was strong stuff, of course. It would have earned me a fame in the village which I little desired.

As punishment I had to copy out the cleansing of the temple from the school Bible. I tried to explain to the teacher that it had been my turn to serve at the altar. But hardly had I opened my mouth when he commanded me even louder to copy the passage twice. He would teach me Christian behaviour, of that I could be sure! With a stick, if necessary. This was a challenge indeed! I defended myself no less vociferously, but I had underestimated our teacher's righteous anger.

"You'll write it out three times, you rascal! And if that still isn't enough, you only have to say so!" Ruler in hand, he came towards me.

I said nothing more. But out of defiance I held out my hand, palm upwards. He hit it three times with the ruler and walked back growling to his desk, which stood on a podium. He took out a notebook and scribbled something in it. In between he gave me angry looks.

The two following Sundays I wrote out the story of the cleansing of the temple three times. It struck me that Jesus

191

too had argued with the tradesmen in the temple. That coudn't have been very peaceful either. The Lord had driven his adversaries from the temple with a whip in his hand. This only confirmed my suspicion that I had been punished unjustly.

Run of bad luck

It never rains but it pours. A trite little proverb, but one based on experience. Probably someone who's been beaten behaves differently from someone who hasn't. He's nervous, distracted, uncertain, depressed. And that can act like a magnet attracting new misfortunes.

Father had bought the mill at the auction. That in itself was not a misfortune. What was a misfortune was that he had to pay for it in autumn, making a hole in the cigar box in which he kept the money for the winter. It was bad luck that we lost Strobel and could not slaughter enough animals. And it was certainly bad luck that the first heavy snowfall caused the roof of the barn in the Schweigmatte to collapse, burying valuable hay under heavy slabs and beams.

That was not the end of our unlucky streak. Tschäggi, our good milch cow, began to suffer from an insidious ailment. It was pitiful to see her wasting away. Mother tried everything to save her. The farmers helped with word and deed. But it was all in vain; the cow was doomed. We ought to have slaughtered her at once. But who slaughters his only milch cow? True, we still had Stärri, the old cow. But she gave very little milk. She was designated for our next home-slaughtering day. The only vet in the area lived in Visp. The railway had long since discontinued its summer service. We had to do without his help.

Mother thought the cow must have swallowed a piece of glass with her hay. It had got stuck, explaining why Tschäggi found it so hard to eat. Mother tried once more to enlist the help of St. Anthony, but the holy man was obviously otherwise engaged. The end result of too much doctoring and hoping was that the animal expired. This we realised too late. The cow could no longer be slaughtered. The meat was worthless, and this was a major misfortune!

Most farmers probably had an insurance for such situations. But to Father insurance policies were like a red rag to a bull. We had no money to buy another cow.

During the winter Zermatt offered few opportunities to earn. Father did carpentry for our own use. Now and then he worked as a glazier. The few panes that got broken in the village were in inn windows and doors. In those cases Father usually left his earnings at their place of origin. "You have to re-invest something when you get an order," was his business principle.

Father often sat for hours on his chair scraping his shoes on the floor. He had little comfort for us:

"We can soon hang our hungry mouths on the nail!" he said. Ropes, chains, a rucksack and other things hung from a nail in the wall behind the front door. It was a long, dangerous nail. I couldn't imagine how we were to hang our hungry mouths on it. All the same, it impressed me. Each time I passed I gave it a nervous look. I noticed Mother often leafing through the newspaper at that time. Normally she hardly looked at newspapers. She preferred to immerse herself in her book on the lives of martyrs and saints if she had time.

One day she came across an advert in the "Valais Messenger". The cantonal hospital in Geneva wanted an assistant cook for some months. She hurried to Father with it. But his male pride would not allow Mother to apply for the post. On the contrary, he raised his voice. Mother stayed calm. She knew we had no other choice. To keep the family above water for the rest of the winter, someone had to earn. It was impossible for Father to find a job. Even young men with healthy hands were condemned to idleness. "What else did I learn French and cooking for at the convent?" she asked.

In the evening Father sat down at the living-room table to write to the hospital in Geneva. We waited for the answer with mixed feelings. Not much was spoken during those days. Then the letter came. The postman brought it into the kitchen. He too was waiting to hear the answer. Mother was offered the job. A miracle! Father had to hurry to the post office to send a telegram accepting the post, so that it would not be given to someone else.

In winter the journey down the valley was very arduous. Kronig, the postman, offered to take Mother down on the horse-drawn sleigh together with the letters and parcels. He would also see to it that his colleagues who operated a mule service between Sankt Niklaus and Stalden took Mother's luggage. Between Stalden and Visp, a postcoach took passengers.

Fresh snow fell during the night. As our family waited in front of the post building, the sun broke through the cloud and dazzled us. It gave us an excuse to cover our eyes. I carried Mother's little case to the post sleigh. The old village curate was there too. He said: "Needs must when the devil drives. Keep your chin up, Barbara!" We all wept. The sleigh had disappeared behind the hill and the mule bells could no longer be heard: but still we stood there.

Father returned with us to the flat. Lina carried our youngest brother in her arms. We had nothing to say. People looked at us out of the corners of their eyes or from under the brims of their hats.

Lina was still a schoolgirl. She set about the domestic chores with great zeal: cooking, bed-making, washing. She also had to look after the animals. She did all this as well as attending school. Father acted as baby-sitter and helped us with our homework. Often he would play cards with us. Now and then, on written instructions from Mother, he would comb our short hair. Mother knew that lice were at large in the school months and needed checking from time to time. Often splendid specimens came to light.

Every month a letter arrived from Geneva. Father pocketed the enclosed banknotes and read out the letter. Then he sat absently on his chair for a while. He felt humiliated. Lina clattered at the stove. We looked at the table or out of the window, trying to be brave as Mother had asked.

Mother was the first wife who had had to leave her family in winter to earn money away from the village. It was especially hard for her as her youngest child could hardly stand. It was commonplace for married men to seek work in autumn as wood-cutters, building labourers, hotel porters, dishwashers or in mines or tunnel works, but the women stayed at home. Hence, Father went into the village as little as possible. And never to a pub. He bridled at the fate that had cost him hand and foot on the first ascent of the Huascaran. Too high a price, as it now proved. At Christmas we received a large parcel: socks knitted by Mother for Father, pullovers for Rudolf and me. My sister was given underwear and my little brother even got a teddy bear. There were apples and nuts as well. What a surprise. After our soup we nibbled the delicacies. Father played cards with us. Before midnight mass my sister made mulled wine, and even we children were given a watered-down glass.

As the church bells rang for midnight mass, we were all in good spirits. According to an old custom, Father left the light burning in the living room. A lamp burned in all the Zermatt living-rooms throughout the night. Outside fell large flakes of snow. The narrow streets were badly lit. From all directions came people with lighted lanterns. They wished each other happy Christmas and plodded off towards the church.

By the side altar a large crib had been set up. Baby Jesus lay on real straw, protected by Mary and Joseph and the animals, who gave him warmth. At the end of mass the congregation sang "Silent night, holy night". We knew that Mother was also attending a midnight mass at the same time. That comforted us.

The suspender belt

Mother liked her work in the hospital kitchen. The nurses treated her kindly. In the evenings some of them always sat with her. She was asked to tell them about her children, her husband and life in the mountains. She liked to talk. It helped to pass the long evenings.

She often lay awake at night. "Why does the Lord send me so much trouble?" she wondered. "Did I turn up my nose at his plans for me? Now I've got it – the worldly life!"

She put all her hopes in her children's futures. They were to have a better life. For her little ones no sacrifice was too great. But it surprised her that there was so much suffering in the world. And something else bothered her: injustice. You met it everywhere.

"Why is there so much injustice with a kind and just God watching over everything?" she wondered.

She was especially fond of Sister Andrea. She told her that her stay in Geneva seemed like a holiday to her. She confided even more:

"I don't think it will do my husband any harm to see how I have spoiled him and how much I do for him." Her brown eyes twinkled and she smiled mischievously.

But when spring awoke in the hospital garden by Lake Geneva, she could hardly wait for the day when she would be able to return to her loved ones. The hospital was very pleased with her work. The matron helped her get some extra wages and a holiday allowance.

"This will be enough money to buy a young cow." Barbara wanted this to be a surprise for her husband. She had every reason to look forward to the reunion.

In Zermatt, too, there were more and more signs of awakening spring. The Foehn burst into the valley and howled in the woods. It peeled the snow from whole slopes, licked the roads clean and opened the crocuses, which covered the meadows like a white carpet. We knew: now Mother must come. And she came.

We sat with her in the kitchen until late at night. We hugged each other again and again. She revealed to Father that she had brought him a big surprise. She would not say what it was, no matter how hard we pressed her. Father found it difficult to adjust to the role of the one receiving presents. Finally she sent us to bed, as she wanted to clear up the kitchen. Father stayed with her.

I heard my parents come into the main room and undress. Father always dropped his shoes on the floor. Suddenly he asked in a very brusque tone:

"What's that contraption you're wearing? I never saw one of those before."

"It's a suspender belt. Much more comfortable than garters, which don't even keep the stockings up."

"Where did you get hold of it?"

"I bought it. Where else should I get it?"

"In Geneva?"

"Of course. Anyway, it wasn't at all expensive."

"I don't mind about that. Stupid, useless rubbish! Of course in Geneva. We know about Geneva. Worse than Paris. Crawling with cheap women. You think I give a damn about it?"

Was he jealous because Mother was wearing a modern suspender belt, or had he a bad conscience because he hadn't shown enough appreciation of what she had done? Father's reactions were not always easy to fathom. Often, when he wanted to show he was pleased and grateful, he would tease and reproach.

"I don't mind at all. If you want to throw money away on rubbish like that, carry on." He threw himself down on the bed as noisily as possible, as if in protest. One of the springs in the mattress jangled. That was the only answer to be heard. Mother put on her nightdress without a word. She came into our room through the open connecting door. She looked to see if we were properly covered. In the pull-out bed I shared with Rudolf she tucked the blanket under the mattress. She noticed I was still awake.

"You must sleep now," she said softly. I felt that she had wet cheeks and whispered into her ear: "You'll go on wearing it, won't you. I mean, hidden!" She bit her bottom lip with her dazzling teeth and smiled agreement, while a stray tear ran down beside her snub nose. Then she went back into the living room, put out the light and got into bed. She climbed over Father into her corner; as always, he claimed the outside. I heard her say:

"You haven't left me any room. You must get used to sharing the bed with me again." She said it in a friendly voice. Father whispered something to her. Then they both laughed.

The great feast

Father had built our house himself. He liked big kitchens.Not surprisingly, ours became the centre of our family life. Not only was the cooking and eating done here. Mother bore her children in the kitchen. It was warm, with hot water to hand.

After the evening meal we would stay at our seats and talk about everyday affairs. If the mood was good, my sister and I sang "The Munot Bell", "The Polish Maid", "The Village Fair", or whatever else was in fashion. In two parts, of course, and with all the necessary fervour. We were dealing with love, faithlessness and pain, after all. These were the things which touched the heart.

The wood-stove, in which the fire crackled all day, kept us warm. Mother knew how to keep it burning between meals with very little wood. The stone-stove in the living room was only lit on very cold days.

The firewood had to be fetched from the shed two floors below, and the water from the well by the Triftbach. Everyone had to do this. The only sanitary facilities were to be found in the Grand Hotel. At that time the age of technological "progress" had only touched us with its fingertips. We enjoyed the luxury of one electric light. It hung on a hook above the dining table, with an enamel plate as a shade. A naked bulb burned at the centre. It sent a rather tremulous light towards the stove and into the corner, where a large wash-basin stood on a wooden frame. There the members of the family wetted their faces in the morning. Any considerable fall of snow affected the brightness of the bulb. Sometimes it cut the power completely.

Mother always had a candle within easy reach. She also needed it to fetch things from the store-room in the evening. The electricity meter had not yet made its appearance. You paid 15 francs a year per lamp. Whether it was on a lot or little made no difference. Father declared: "With such horrendous electricity prices I can't install lamps in the store-room and the WC as well! I'm not the emperor of China."

Uncle Arnold shared this point of view. He had cut an opening in the wooden panelling near the ceiling and hung a lamp in it. Half of it lit the kitchen and half the next room. He was proud of his achievement. Mother found this sort of economy dreary. She would rather have one room well lit.

In the north wall of the kitchen two windows gave on to a rocky slope, on which our neighbour Marinus had planted a potato field. Our hens came to this window to beg a handful of left-overs from Mother during the day.

Once a year, the evening before the feast of Corpus Christi, the kitchen served as a bathroom. In the absence of a bathtub Mother put the big wash-tub on the floor. Before going to bed, the smaller children had to appear one by one in their nightshirts.

At that hour the firewood crackled more loudly than usual in the stove. The steam from the kettle spiralled up to the wooden ceiling. There it formed large drops that fell sizzling on to the hotplate and rose again as little puffs of steam. No wonder the kitchen windows were steamed up and began to weep.

All this served to lighten our anticipation of the forthcoming feast.

Anticipation is, as we know, the keenest form of enjoyment. It is untarnished by the weight of reality and often bound with some sort of ritual. In our case it was that of bathing.

"All right, off with your shirt! Now for a bit of thorough scrubbing," said Mother. I had to sit in the tub. She washed my back, arms, legs and head. She did not go about it particularly gently. The rest was done standing up. That is how it always was on the eve of Corpus Christi. "You must be clean inside and out, otherwise God won't take any pleasure in you." And I was clean inside and out! In the late afternoon she had sent me to confession to pluck my soul from the sink of iniquity. But bodily cleanliness was no less important.

In the morning I put on my new suit. Father had ordered the material C.O.D. from a mail-order firm. It was "devil's skin", reputed to be untearable. Out of the velvet-like, midnight-blue cloth the seamstress, who came to our house to sew, made a jacket and a calf-length pair of trousers. She insisted that the jacket should have mother-of-pearl buttons, which put me in an unenviable position with my comrades.

I crept to church along back alleys. If anyone met me, I put on a self-conscious smile and brushed my hand awkwardly over my jacket pocket. "Aha, Hannes has got a new suit. Well I never. And mother-of-pearl buttons too. Just look at that!" Thus they baited me. And I stood there embarrassed, bowing my head and scraping the ground with my shoes.

The din of the bells was thundering from the church tower when I finally dared join the throng of children in the church square. Soldiers were parading, the village band playing, and in the church porch the sexton appeared with an armful of canton flags fluttering on wooden poles. With a veritable battle-cry the boys descended on the defenceless sexton. Every boy wanted to march behind the soldiers as a canton cadet. Anyone who could not get hold of a flag had to walk primly with the prayerful procession. The sexton, who had been instructed by the priest to hand out the flags in an orderly manner, found himself pressed against the church wall. Against the seething pack he was powerless.

A particularly violent struggle was waged over the Valais flag. But similar duels flared up over any other desirable emblem. I had grabbed hold of the Aargau flag at the same moment as Roby Julen, of whom it was said that he drank a litre of goat's milk every day, which was why he was so strong. The triple-starred banner became the object of a fight to the bitter end, the flagpole being an early casualty. That did not mean the question of ownership was resolved. Ears and hair had to be brought into play, arms and legs enlisted to the cause. My devil's skin made its first acquaintance with the rough and dusty surface of the church square. The seamstress had used too flimsy thread to hold the buttons. And the skin was far from tear-proof, as a triangular flap at the knee was soon to demonstrate. Anything worse was averted by the hasty arrival of the teacher, who resolved the conflict by awarding to each party what they had conquered: to Roby the two pieces of the pole and to me the flag itself. Luckily, a short stump of pole was visible below the cloth, allowing me to take my place behind the soldiers.

Blissfully I waved my tattered flag. Then I caught the sorrowful eye of my mother in the ranks of the praying women, a first drop of bitterness entered my cup of joy. But the village band was playing the flag-march; the priest carrying the golden monstrance from the church to its position under the canopy held by four white-gloved parish councillors; the officer gave the command to shoulder arms; the church choir diligently attacked the Credo: and from the ranks of the faithful the prayers murmured and growled towards a crescendo. The church bells vied with the rest of the heavenly uproar, and the procession set off down the village street.

Before the windows and on the steps glowed flowering plants. The sun whetted its rays on the copper pots, the silver cross, the monstrance and the fixed bayonets of the grenadiers. The altars set up before the hotels gave off a scent of globeflowers, marguerites and alpine roses. Garlands of pine and larch twigs, adorned with colourful paper flowers, flapped in the breeze of the glorious June

Sunday, vying with the flags and banners of the richly decorated street.

Before each altar the procession stopped. The buzz of prayer died away. The people went down on their knees. The priest, with chanting voice and the Holy of Holies in his hands, called down the blessing of heaven. The church choir sang at the top of their voices. The brass band played the flag-march; the grenadiers fired off their salvoes; and high on the rocky slopes the gun salutes crashed, re-echoing from valley to valley, as if the god of thunder were coming down the mountain in person.

This wondrous spectacle lifted my soul quite out of my body. With the other boys I waved my flag and felt my boyish heart leaping in my throat. To admire white-dressed girls, to smile in pity on altar-boys while marching proudly behind the soldiers was the acme of earthly joy. What, beside that, were a few missing mother-or-pearl buttons, a triangular rip in my trouser leg, dishevelled hair and a face dirty from a scuffle? Even Mother's reproachful look was forgotten. Music, soldiers, song and bell-chimes bore up my mood along the flower-decked street to the next altar, where the spectacle of the priestly blessing was repeated with all its attendant splendours. And so on, until the tour brought the participants back to the church square.

The exuberant, festive mood was not carried with the flags into the church, there to be enclosed, but surged on through the village streets. The children's spirits rose higher and higher. The mothers were in good spirits and the fathers were looking forward to free wine. Each family was entitled to a litre of red wine at the parish's expense. The juice of the vine trickled in a constant stream from a large barrel in the cellar of the parish hall into bottles, jugs and pans. It was usually drunk, unaided, by the head of the family. Despite this, some precocious lads managed to get their first taste of tipsiness. Now and then tempers flared at one pub or another as the afternoon wore on, for an excess of wine is known to make people aggressive, to cast out inhibitions. To spare me the birch rod on my bare behind on such a festive day, my mother hushed up my mishap with the devil's skin. I changed into my weekday clothes before our midday meal. Helpfully, I fetched Father's jug of free wine. Addressing himself to the roast veal and the red wine, he failed to notice my change of clothing.

After vespers the villagers chatted in the square. Some paraded up and down the main street in new clothes, having been shown insufficient attention earlier in the day. The boys romped in the school playground, played catch or showed off their skills on the horizontal bar. Some of them showed a lot of pluck.

I stood in my ordinary clothes by the Triftbach bridge. Mother had taken my Sunday suit back to the seamstress. She was to try to put it back in order. Without letting me into the secret, she was trying to deflect Father's wrath. I should have liked to join in the gymnastics, but was ashamed to mix with the boys in my get-up. Then Toni, the leading gymnast, noticed me. He came up to me: "Come on, have a go at the grand circle. I'll see you come to no harm."

I went with him gladly to the bar. There was a block of wood by one of the side bars. When we boys stood on it, we could reach the steel tube. I hoisted myself to hip height. Then I arched into the swing and spun three times round the bar, with fairly straight arms. Not much attention was paid to leg position. The knees were straight or bent as the case may be, and the heavy mountain shoes clattered together. I started the last swing slower to stop my body with straight arms above the bar. For a fraction of a second I put my weight on my left arm to twist my right hand round the bar and start my backward swing. This particular exercise – three times forwards and three times backwards – had curiosity value. I needed to earn respect and prestige in my weekday clothes. But it was not to be. Even the first back-swing was irregular. When I tried to put more momentum into the next turn, the fingers of my right hand were pulled open as I went up. I flew in a high arc from the bar, my legs flung into the air, my body bent. I tried to break my fall with my left arm as I landed. It cracked like a branch snapped from a tree. A piercing pain shot through my body. "Mother!" I cried, though she was not among the bystanders.

I lay on the ground. My left arm looked like a crooked stovepipe. Ulna and radius were displaced behind my wrist. I was deathly pale. "Holy Mother of God, you've broken your arm," said Toni, shaken: "We must get you to the doctor."

The long night

Dr. Hörnli was a young doctor. It was his first job in a general practice. People thought it was the same with a doctor as with bread: the fresher the better.

His diploma hung beside the consulting-room door. You could not miss it in its heavy gold frame behind shiny glass. It was written in Latin, which impressed the beholder. Beside the diploma hung a large crucifix. For the doctor was not merely authenticated by a diploma, but a pious Christian and a boyhood friend of the priest's. That inspired confidence.

He put my arm in a plaster. Had the arm not finished swelling, or was the dressing too tight? I dont't know, but I was soon in excruciating pain. My fingers went cold and blue as bilberries. Father sent my little brother to the doctor. He wasn't there. My sister met the crying boy and tracked the doctor down at a neighbour's.

The doctor rocked from his heels to his toes beside my bed and reassured my parents. He made it clear to me with his sceptical smile that he didn't take my pain very seriously. Mother was still worried.

"Aunt Ida thinks the plaster is too tight," she said.

"Really? Does she indeed?" replied the doctor ironically. "Who is this Aunt Ida of yours?"

"My husband's sister. She knows something about medicinal herbs."

"Has she studied for eight years at university as well? Aha. There you are. Your aunt may be a wise woman and can no doubt tell wild wormwood from edelweiss, but I know more about fractures. Or do you perhaps doubt it?" Of course, my parents did not doubt the competence of such a highly qualified and pious doctor.

"I have done whatever there had to be done. The good Lord must provide the cure. But the boy must show us what he's made of," he opined, without taking much notice of my arm. He took his leave and floated out of the door.

During the night the pain got worse. At times I lost consciousness. The whole family stood around my bed in their nightshirts.

"I can't stand here any longer," said Mother. "We must send for the doctor."

"Now, in the middle of the night? We can't do that." Father replied.

I was sick again. Mother took the towel and dried my face. "Try to drink a little tea, Hannes dear."

"Leave me in peace!" I shouted. "Go back to bed."

"Yes, get some sleep," said Mother. "I'll stay up."

"No, Mother, it disturbs me. I don't want anyone looking at me. I don't like it."

Mother made a worried face. She shook my pillows, covered the glass lampshade with a handkerchief and went back to bed.

I couldn't sleep. No matter how I lay, it wasn't right. I tossed about. I felt my pulse beating violently in my neck, and a piercing pain ran from my chest to my arm. The endless ticking of the wall-clock got on my nerves. I clenched my teeth. I bit my lips. I bit above my lips.

I felt sweat trickling behind my ears. A salty coating formed on my tongue. I felt sick again. Then everything started going round. A red light fanned before my eyes. It turned emerald green and purplish blue. I lost consciousness.

"Heavens," said Mother in the morning. "What a sight you are! What have you done with your lips? They're all raw. What's the matter with you, Hannes darling?"

The doctor arrived in the early afternoon. He had a fat tome under his arm. One of the innumerable volumes he had used at the University of Berne. Father marvelled at the colour plates showing the inside of an arm.

"Looks like a photograph of an arm that's been opened up. Everything so clear. Science has really made great strides."

The doctor gave a lecture. He knew all the bones, muscles and tendons by name, as if they were fellow members of a club. Mother stood beside the bed. Her lips twitched. Suddenly she asked fearfully: "Why are his fingers still so cold and blue? I covered them with a warm wool scarf, but they haven't changed."

"Patience, dear lady. The boy's getting better. The arm doesn't hurt so much as last night, does it, my boy? There you are! Just takes a little time. I could cut the plaster open, but then I'd have to tie the cast back on with a bandage, and I haven't one with me. I haven't got the plaster shears here either."

"We have bandages in the house, Doctor," said Mother, "and Rudolf can fetch the shears."

"No need, no need, dear lady. I have my army knife with me. I take it wherever I go. It will serve the purpose."

He took a knife out of his pocket, the sort I had always wanted. He opened a big blade and sat down on the bed. The pillows were straightened; and the doctor tried to cut open the plaster. He scratched with the blade from the elbow towards the wrist. The first two centimetres went all right. Then he cut into the flesh. Blood seeped out and discoloured the plaster.

"Dear me, it's not working. Never mind. Nothing to worry about. I'll call back tomorrow with the shears."

She of little faith

Next day Dr Hörnli arrived with the plaster shears. Mother listened mistrustfully to his usual patter. He sat on the bed and snipped at the plaster till it opened lengthways.

Curious to catch a glimpse of my arm, I lifted my head from the pillow. In the gap in the plaster, the skin of the arm was dark brown. In some places watery shreds of dead skin stuck to the cotton-wool padding. They hung like wet tissue paper from the cut edges of the plaster. Where the thumb joined the hand there was a dark patch of congealed blood. My head slumped back onto the pillow. I felt a stabbing pain in my arm. Then gradually it eased. The excruciating sense of constriction passed away. For the first time I felt hungry again.

I asked for something to eat, preferably a saveloy sausage. Mother hurried to the village shop. But when she got back, my hunger had gone. Mother was disappointed. "A pity the train isn't running yet, or Father would take you to hospital."

"I don't want to go to hospital. I'm feeling much better. My arm will be all right, I can feel it."

A worried look came into Mother's dark-brown eyes. She sighed softly and withdrew to the kitchen.

In the early afternoon I was dozing while Mother sat by my bed darning socks. Suddenly there was a knock at the door. Knocking on a door was an alien custom among us. It meant the same as standing outside the door and shouting: "Watch out, I'm coming in. I know you've got something to hide. Hide the loot quickly, so that I can come in. You're highly suspect riff-raff." However, knocking was allowed as a joke. You would mumble some disjointed English into your beard to make the people think they were getting a visitor and give them a fright. Afterwards you would have a good laugh, or set about the intruder.

Mother must have thought it was a joke of that sort, for she called out: "Come on in. It's not a billy goat, is it?"

The black-haired head of the priest appeared round the door. While we all chuckled, Mother was embarrassed at having received the reverend gentleman so impolitely. She apologised, but even she could not suppress a laugh.

I was the object of this solemn visit. According to Christian custom, the priest paid a visit to sick members of his flock. Mother mentioned her concern. She described the strange appearance of the skin and the dark blood clot below the thumb.

"You're causing yourself needless distress, Barbara," said the priest. "God does not allow his children to fall into the abyss. He'll take care of your boy. And how is the patient?"

"Since the doctor cut open the plaster, I've been feeling better, thank you, Father."

"There you are. Dr. Hörnli is an excellent doctor. He has a very distinguished diploma."

"I've seen it. It's got a gold frame," I agreed.

"He devotes himself unsparingly to his patients," the priest eulogised.

"I've nothing against him," Mother replied. "But the arm looks bad. It may be sinful of me, but we're very worried about it."

"You've always been a God-fearing woman, Barbara. Why have you suddenly lost your trust in God? What more must He do to make us believe in His loving care? He led the people of Israel our of their servitude in Egypt to the Promised Land, parted the seas, caused water to spring from the rocks of the desert, sent manna from Heaven to feed His Israelite children. And you don't believe He will help your child?"

Mother felt chastened. What kind of a Christian was she? Hardly more faith than a heathen! Suspicious of a pious doctor. She nodded her head slightly. But she did not reply. She knew that the priest and the doctor were good friends.

To break the awkward silence she said finally: "Perhaps we are worrying too much."

"That will only damage your health. Dr. Hörnli will have the boy on his feet again. He's done far more important things than that."

Mother recalled the young wife who had died in childbirth recently. She moistened her lips with her tongue. But she did not say anything.

And I was soon back on my feet. First I sat in the sun on the balcony, resting my arm on a pillow; then I could put it in a sling and parade about the streets of the upper village.

In those days the inhabitants of Zermatt were still one big community. There were no secrets, or very few. It was almost impossible to conceal something from the neighbours' eyes. Each villager's life lay open like a book in a window display. You could leaf through it at will, sometimes finding out things you did not want to know. Everyone knew who was working with drill or pick in which mine or tunnel, how much he earned, and how much of that he sent home every fortnight. Whether someone's family drank skimmed milk or full cream milk at home. How far a family was in debt at the Konsum. And of course, how the hip, back or eye-tooth was bearing up at this time of year. You knew when this or that holiday guest was to arrive, which mountains he would climb and how much he usually tipped. Everything was talked and gossiped about. People were open with each other. They told each other almost everything. And what was not told, you found out through the thin boards that served one apartment as a ceiling and another as a floor. No-one could take a step in his home without it being heard above or below. Everyone wore his true face on his shoulders. Pretence was impossible.

Naturally, all the inhabitants of the village knew about my arm. I had to repeat the latest news about it countless times in every street, whenever I met someone who had a gap in their information. I therefore took pains to take my arm out of the sling very early on and hide as much as possible of it in my trouser pocket to curtail curiosity.

Secret mission

The railway had resumed its summer service. High-spirited engines tugged red carriages along the valley, barking like old St. Bernard dogs and trailing a plume of smoke over the carriage roofs. They arrived hissing at the station. When they stopped with a screech beside us boys, they stood sulking to themselves, as if the engine driver and fireman had overworked them again. Now and then they would emit a puff of steam from some hidden pipe. We would start back if we had put our noses too close to the polished copper; or, as we peered at the mechanism underneath the far from lifeless monster, it would startle us by letting out a stream of hot water.

As the iron horse manoeuvred in the station, we would run after it, noting the driver's every move, so that we would later be able to drive the "Breithorn", the "Monte Rosa", the "Furka" or whatever else the steam engines had inscribed on their shining brass name-plates. I believe many of us would have been able to set the locomotives in motion and stop them again, such was our enthusiasm for those steel dragons.

The hoteliers opened up the big buildings, the grand hotels, annexes and guest-houses. The army of employees appeared. The concierges, guides, porters, lift-boys, commissionaires, cooks, sauciers, entremétiers, casse-rolliers, waitresses and head waiters, cellarmen and chambermaids, and all the others. Shopkeepers set out their displays, rubbed their hands and raised hopeful eyes to the god of the weather.

Like exotic butterflies, the first visitors alighted. Undemanding Englishmen as lean as rakes, perfumed French ladies, German gentlemen with the obligatory crew cut, and modest "Grüezi"-Swiss, who greeted everyone they passed on their walks. For the short summer season Zermatt was again in touch with the great world.

In hobnailed shoes, with my sick arm in my pocket, I ambled towards the summer that had started so inauspiciously. Mother had given up her post as cook at the Matterhorn cabin to have me near her. Lina went up to the Kalbermatte with my younger brother, while Mother looked after the little tea-room in Zumsee with me and my baby brother.

When I awoke one morning, I again had the salty coating on my tongue. I carefully took my arm from under the blanket, and shrank back in horror. The fingers were protruding from the bandage like swollen sausages. My pulse beat violently in my arm and a stabbing pain came from near my armpit.

Mother again looked worried. She gave me a thick slice of toast for breakfast and sent me to the doctor in Zermatt. He was not at all pleased with me:

"A nice mess we have here! You've got yourself an infection. Now what do we do? I'll have to cut it open."

Where the swellings had formed he made two cuts, each a centimetre long. What came out made my throat go tight. I was instructed to bathe the arm daily in camomile tea. But the infection persisted. It even got worse. As I lay in bed one evening resting my arm on my chest, something started dripping from the bandage. Mother became very alarmed. She took me to the doctor and demanded an examination by a hospital doctor. Dr. Hörnli would not hear of it. He guaranteed that the infection would soon subside. Without his agreement the medical insurance refused to contribute to hospital costs.

It was a hot summer day. Mother had put out the hot camomile bath on the balcony in front of the kitchen. I was in the water closet. On such days I could prolong my visits there. The wind from the valley blew through the hole in the floor. It played across my naked behind with an agreeable cooling effect. In the nearby meadow throngs of grasshoppers chirruped, and everywhere buzzed bumble-bees, wasps and flies. It sounded like the plucking and scraping of countless stringed instruments. I took my time, feeling the breeze and listening to the drowsy humming.

"The bath's getting cold," Mother scolded.

I broke off the sitting, took the bandages and plaster from my arm and immersed my arm in the daily camomile bath on the balcony.

In Zumsee there were always a lot of flies. They not only revelled in the copious dung-heaps, but also liked blooming nettles, warm wooden beams, living-room ceilings and window panes. Everywhere they found scope for their impudent pestering.

That day I was their special target. They all seemed to have decided to rendez-vous on our balcony, swarming in from all sides. Some were so persistent that they fell into the bath and floundered noisily.

In one of the wounds I found the end of a string. When I got hold of it, I pulled out a piece of pus-covered tendon three centimetres long. That troubled me, but I said nothing about it to Mother. She was worried enough as it was.

She came out of the kitchen, saw the mass of flies annoying me and set about them angrily with her dish-cloth. They retreated for a few moments, then came back with renewed determination. I looked on at the unequal struggle for a while, then I said, without really meaning to: "Let them be, Mother. It's not their fault I'm slowly rotting away."

Mother paused for a moment. She was standing behind my back. I could tell that my words had upset her. She went back slowly into the kitchen. Then quiet reigned in the house. Only the buzzing of flies and the chirping of grasshoppers in the summer meadow could be heard. I knew that Mother was standing at the kitchen table, soaking the sleeve of her overall with tears.

After a while she came back. Her eyes were still glistening, but her carriage showed determination.

"Listen, my poor boy," she said. "I have a distant relative in Sierre. He's a doctor. We're going to see him tomorrow. We've got to find out what's the matter with your arm. I can't stand by doing nothing any more."

A neighbour offered to look after my little brother and the chickens for a day. Early next morning we surprised my father in his little room over our Zermatt hen-run. He called this lodging his "summer residence".

"I'm glad you're going to another doctor. Only Dr. Hörnli must know nothing about it. Otherwise he could make things difficult for us."

Mother and I did not take the main street to get to the station. We crept like thieves behind hotels and tennis courts, down narrow back-alleys. To look normal and not attract attention, Mother carried her black plumed hat and handbag in a paper bag.

When Mother had bought the tickets, we went onto the platform. My favourite engine, the "Breithorn", stood muttering quietly to itself in its green hunting suit, with its black boiler and shining pistons and wheels, and two red carriages behind.

We sat down close to the engine. I leant out of the window so that I wouldn't miss a single move by the driver. After all, this was a serious occasion: I had never travelled by train before. Mother kept tugging me back inside the carriage by my coat. She looked very genteel. She was now wearing her hat with the feathers and her finely knitted black gloves. She held her handbag tightly under her arm. She felt at ease, as our trip was to take us past her home village of Turtmann. A short visit to her brother Toni was planned, if there was time, on the way back.

The shrilling of the station-master's whistle roused the "Breithorn" from her reverie. She replied with a long exuberant blast of her whistle. Our heads were jerked backwards. Luckily they were firmly attached. We felt the powerful, pulsing tug of the engine and heard her bark grow faster and faster. Smoke came in through the window. The gentleman next to us demanded that it be shut. I sat next to Mother, peering through the glass. It looked as if the carriage was standing still and the trees, bushes and rocks were rushing past. The hamlets of Gaden and Stadel danced along the valley. The farmers stopped work in the fields to gaze at the chugging train. A ghostly hand shook our heads, pressed us against the back of the seat or the side of the carriage. We looked at each other, laughing at our helplessness. As we approached the river, I caught my breath. The embankment suddenly stopped. The "Breithorn" seemed to be plunging into a chasm. Taking a gigantic leap, it just managed to land on the other side, where it continued puffing along as if nothing had happened. Cows grazing near the rails were scattered by a blast of the whistle, charging away with lifted tails.

I remembered our animals on the pasture and fell silent. For a while I sat quietly next to Mother, letting the invisible hand press me against the seat, the side of the carriage, or Mother.

She put her hand on my shoulder:

"You can have faith in the doctor we're going to. His great-grandfather was my great-grandfather. He was governor of Sierre. An important person."

She did not want to boast, but could not quite hide her pride in having had an influential great-grandfather. With mixed feelings we travelled towards the Rhone valley.

The doctor in Sierre did not keep us waiting. He was very courteous to Mother and talked to her about their relations. When he noticed she could speak French, he spoke to her in that language.

He examined fluid taken from my arm under a microscope. I noticed him discover something that seemed to take him aback. He spoke about it to Mother, and her face grew visibly graver. A shadow seemed to spread over it. I thought I could catch two words: "hôpital" and "amputation". I caught my breath. A fine relation! And Mother wants me to have faith in someone like that!

When we were outside the doctor's house, where a rose border flanked the path to the gate, I turned on Mother:

"I'm not having my arm cut off! And I'm not going to hospital. Just so that you know!"

Mother could not conceal her surprise.

"But ... who says anything about that? That's nonsense, Hannes, dear.."

"I understood what you were saying. He talked about 'amputation'. And 'hôpital'. Do you think I'd go to a hospital to have my arm cut off? You must be mad!"

"Now just calm down, my boy. The doctor has found out that the bones have been attacked by the infection. They've been eaten away. He says no amount of bathing will help now. But he knows a doctor in Lausanne. A Professor Nicole. He says we should entrust ourselves to him. He could save the arm. But if we do nothing, then..."

Mother paused. She looked at me helplessly, pursing her lips. I threw myself into her arms. We stood like that for a while. We did not need to look at each other. I heard Mother's heart beating. We took our time till we felt the gravel under our shoes again.

Mother no longer wanted to visit her brother Toni, but to go back to Zermatt as fast as possible.

The blue hour

Since he had heard about the visit to the doctor, Father had had great difficulty taking the museum visitors round the memorial gallery and telling the story of the accidents. The words stuck in his throat. He found his explanations trivial and meaningless. He kept coming back unintentionally to his own worries. Especially with Swiss visitors. They often showed sympathy for the son whom the doctor had refused to send to hospital. The case was talked about in hotel lobbies. A doctor from Solothurn was prepared to take the matter up. He knew a well-known senior consultant at the children's hospital in Berne and discussed the affair with him. A few days later I visited Professor Matti at the Hotel Riffelalp.

He received me at a window seat in the big hall of the hotel. As I told him how the accident had happened and who had been standing nearby, he said with a smile: "Show me your arm, that's more important." I took off my jacket. He wanted to take the dressing off himself.

There were no people near us. Only the Matterhorn looked on through the big veranda window. The mountain lay in the blue afternoon haze, its outlines soft and dreamy. We called this time of day the blue hour.

"Uh-huh. That doesn't look too good," said the professor. "Something has to be done as soon as possible."

What had to be done he did not say. I too had nothing to say. I just thought: "He wants to send me to a hospital."

"I'm here for two more weeks. Then I start work again at the children's hospital," he went on. "Would you like to come to Berne with me?"

"Dr. Hörnli doesn't think I need to go to hospital," I stammered. "He says I'll be well again in two months."

"He thinks so, does he? In two months it could be too late."

I stood there, not knowing what else to say. I bit my bottom lip.

"Don't you worry. I'll talk to Dr. Hörnli. I know him. It will be all right. But you have to ask your father if he agrees. Then he can take you to Berne. Here's the address of the hospital. But he should telephone first."

"I don't want to have…"

"What don't you want? Tell me. I don't mind."

"To have my arm ampatated." I stumbled over the wretched foreign word.

"Who says anything about amputating?"

"Aunt Ida said that if it goes on like this I'll have to have it ampatated – she said so."

"We want to save your arm, not amputate it. Don't we? So that's what we'll do."

I nodded doubtfully. "You see, I need the arm. I want to be a mountain guide."

"I can understand that. It's a fine profession." The professor put my plaster back on and stroked my cheek as he said goodbye.

In the hotel doorway I stopped and looked hopefully up at the Matterhorn. On the Zmuttgrat patches of spring snow glistened, and in a hollow of the Tiefmatten glacier was a copper glow like distant yearning, amid the darkness of the North Face.

An old man had once said to me: "If someone has to go to hospital, you know what's coming to him." And he nodded meaningfully. I knew what he meant, for the same thing happened to everyone who went there. Still, they were usually old, and I was young. And I wanted to be a mountain guide.

Up among the peaks the cold mountain gloom was already settling.

Sister Klara

"You can get undressed."

Surprised, I looked towards the window. Sunlight was flooding through the orange blinds on the terrace. It was still bright daylight. "We have to take a bath," Sister Klara explained. She tried to open my case. Because of a faulty catch the lid was secured with a piece of string.

Sister Klara, in her blue deaconess dress with white spots, put the few clothes I had brought with me into the chest. Her dark hair was parted under her white cap and only showed above her forehead. She stayed in the room while I undressed.

"Haven't you got a dressing-gown?"

"Only women wear gowns."

Sister Klara laughed. "All right, you can do without. Now, off with your shirt. You're getting a nice white hospital outfit."

I hesitated. It seemed improper to expose myself. I waited.

"Or shall I help you?"

"No!"

I stood naked before her. As far as my hands allowed, I covered my dawning manhood. She pulled a snow-white nightshirt over my head. It was some time before I noticed that it had a slit at the back and did not cover my behind. I quickly turned round and tried to pinch the hems together with my fingers. Sister Klara did not seem to notice any of this.

My room was connected to the ward by an open door; in the ward were twelve children of various ages. At first I thought I owed the single room to my father's influential friends in Berne, who had brought me to the hospital. The staff had seemed very impressed by their visit. The lady was addressed deferentially as "Frau Bundesrat", meaning that she was the wife of someone high up in politics. I found out later that the allocation of a single room indicated the severity of the impending operation and had little to do with influential friends.

"Hey! You're day-dreaming. Come on, we must go to the bathroom." I followed Sister Klara down a long corridor. With my right hand I clasped the slit in the back of my nightshirt.

White-aproned men and nurses ran about busily, joking and laughing with each other, quite forgetting they were in a hospital where children were suffering. Some doors had a notice saying "No admittance" on them. But there were no notices saying "No laughing", which in my opinion would have been more appropriate in a place with so many sick children.

In front of a blocked-up window stood a big bath-tub. Sister Klara ran the bath. The water poured into the tub in a powerful jet, roaring like the Gornerbach in its ravine far away. At this time we usually had our animals on the Schweigmatte pasture, grazing the hay.

"Don't stand about. I've a lot to do. Come on, take your shirt off."

"I can bathe on my own."

"You can't get the dressing wet. I'll help you. We have to be clean. Tomorrow the consultant wants to see you."

I climbed into the bath, holding my arm cautiously above the water. The sister busied herself about me in a motherly way. That her task was far from superfluous was soon shown by the colour of the water. Bending over me, she scrubbed robustly. I studied her narrow face as it moved back and forth close to my head. Water droplets from the steam adhered to the almost invisible down on her upper lip. The little hairs shone as if sprinkled with dew.

"Is something the matter?" she asked rather gruffly.

I denied it so hotly that she looked at me in astonishment. Then she laughed kindly and ruffled my hair: "I think you're a little scamp."

Soon afterwards I was sitting with two other boys at the big table in the ward. The table-top was covered with patterned waterproof cloth. Our meal was brought into the room on a little trolley. It was still bright daylight.

The other children's pillows were straightened. They sat up in bed. Sister Klara had to feed some of them with noodles and apple puree. The cook had forgotten to toss the noodles in butter and sprinkle grated cheese on them. Instead, she had mixed them with bread crumbs. How could she! The apple puree lacked sugar. My mother cooked very simple fare, but what she put on the table was always first-class.

I tried to feed a little boy who had both hands wrapped in cotton wool and bandages. He thought the food delicious. How could he! The boy told me about his accident. He had severe burns.

The sun was still nesting in the nearby treetops when I had to go to bed in my ridiculous shirt. The room was completely white. The bed was white. The table and chairs were painted white. Even the wash-stand behind the door, with taps from which hot or cold water came as desired, was white. No wood, no beams, no checked curtains and pillowcases, no knots in the ceiling. Everything white, only white, like the inside of an igloo. But the room was big. We could have fitted our cabin on the pasture into it twice over. And what impressed me especially was that the water simply disappeared into the wall below the basin. Heaven knew where it went.

A blackbird was singing in the nearby trees, and from the station you could hear the puffing of locomotives and the clatter of trains. In them sat people who were going home. Now and then the wailing wheels of a tram would interrupt the silence, or the engine of a car would roar briefly. All strange, new noises. In between, church bells struck the hour in various keys.

I lay on my back. It was my first night in the hospital. The ceiling was high above me. Mother will now be in the kitchen, washing up. She probably won't sing much today as she works. And Father will be sitting under a petroleum lamp in the corner, reading the "Valais Messenger". Perhaps he'll also brood a bit and scrape his feet. Homesickness gnawed at my heart.

I had not noticed that Sister Klara was standing by my bed. She had come into the room quietly to see how I was. The face I saw was a blur.

"Aha! I thought as much. You're homesick."

She sat on the bed and took my hand in hers.

"It's always like this on the first day. It will pass. Have you brought anything to read with you? You haven't? What have you read already, then?"

"My schoolbooks."

"Yes, and what else?"

"What else? I once got a book from my sister."

"What was it called?"

"It was a nice book. Sad, but nice. It was called 'Strong Love'. The count was not allowed to marry the poor girl. But she wasn't a poor girl at all. She came from a count's family, only no-one knew..."

Have you read children's books as well?" the nurse interrupted me.

"Do you mean Mass books?"

"No. Books like the ones about the Turnach children?"

"No, we haven't any like that. Only schoolbooks."

"I'll bring you a book tomorrow. It's called 'The Red Scarf'. Do you like reading?"

"I don't know. I like listening to stories. Ghost stories. Or ones about magic animals and things like that."

"Do you know the Brothers Grimm?"

"No, I don't. But my mother does. They came to have tea with her."

"The things you say! Then I'll bring you Grimm's fairy tales tomorrow. You'll enjoy them. Now try to get some sleep." She took my face between her hands and kissed me on the forehead and close to the place where the lips join.

I was happy. With a feeling of joy and trust I threw myself
into the arms of sleep.

Golden skies

There were more shocks before the operation.

"It's your turn tomorrow," I was told. But then it was postponed for a day. Then again it didn't happen. I had to lie in bed worrying from one day to the next. The sister gave me reduced rations each evening. She was very kind to me. To distract my thoughts she gave me a shepherd story by Ernst Wiechert, a popular writer of the time.

I was not to know that the doctor was waiting for an authorisation from my father. The doctor feared the bones might have been too badly damaged by the long infection,which would have left only one possibility. For that he needed my father's consent. This plunged Father into a crisis of conscience. He hesitated two whole days to sign such an authorisation. Everyone in Zumsee had expressed an opinion on the matter. They differed widely. It was left to my father to decide.

When the document finally arrived, everything went very quickly. But the operation lasted four hours. After it there was a slow waking from deep anaesthetic.

The first impressions were confusing. My brief glances fell on a yellow-gold sky. The afternoon sun was lighting up the blinds on the balcony, below which my bed stood. Sister Klara was trying to wake me. When I had fits of vomiting, she raised my head to clear the mucus. She sent the children away when they got too curious, craning their necks and pulling faces. With my healthy arm I tried to pull Sister Klara to me. But my limbs seemed to be filled with lead. She stroked my cheek. Did she know how soothing her soft touch felt to me in that state?

Before the operation Sister Klara had promised me: "No, you certainly won't feel any pain. You'll sleep like an angel – and then it will be over."

"But afterwards? Will I feel pain afterwards?"

"Then I'll be with you again."

Gradually I regained consciousness. I felt utterly wretched from the anaesthetic, but I felt no pain. Suddenly I grew alarmed.

"I've been operated on," I thought. "My arm! What's the matter with my arm? Where is my arm?"

I could only see a mass of bandages. With my right hand I felt fearfully for fingers. I felt the first pain. "Thank God" – there were my fingers. All of them, neatly lined up like hens sleeping on their perch. The tension eased in me. I fell back deep into the pillows. Sister Klara gave a tired, faint smile. She nodded:

"What did I tell you?"

But in her eyes there was not the reassurance I sought.

Sister Klara had a knack of always doing the right thing. The first day after my admission she had sent me into the hospital garden:

"Jump about a bit, then you'll sleep well!"

She could not have known that I had never seen grapes on the vine. On the south side of the hospital wall they hung in rows on an espalier. The dark blue globes were covered in a whitish haze. Wasps buzzed angrily around the sweet berries. The blackbirds, too, scolded because I could not tear myself away from the grapes. I also filled my pockets, as I wanted to give Sister Klara a surprise.

From behind some tall sunflowers the red-headed gardener was watching my insatiable appetite with steel-blue eyes. After a time it became too much for him – not only the piracy of the wasps and blackbirds, but mine as well. He took me to the hospital administrator.

My disgraceful behaviour caused trouble for Sister Klara. As the person responsible for the grape thief, she was summoned to the office. I stood before the administrator, shamefacedly emptying my pockets, while Sister Klara offered to pay for the damage. She took a purse from her skirt pocket.

"That's not what I meant," said the administrator. "Please put it away."

But Sister Klara stood her ground.

"I can't do that. What the boy has taken, I'll make good. I insist. Let the gardener state the price."

The gardener twisted his hat in embarrassment. He shrugged: "Eighty, ninety centimes. I can't say exactly. I didn't weigh them."

Sister Klara took the coins from her purse and put them rather emphatically on the table. Then she took me by the hand and led me from the room.

"How could you fill your pockets as well?" she scolded, when we reached the landing. I said nothing. I couldn't very well tell her I wanted to bring the stolen fruit to her. She stopped and looked up and down the staircase. Then she said quietly:

"Just make sure you don't get caught next time," and she laughed mischievously.

I could hardly believe my ears. A weight was lifted from me. From that moment on I loved Sister Klara.

The other children looked forward to the visiting days. An army of parents, aunts and relations tramped down the long corridors. Carrying food, toys and flowers in string bags and baskets, they deluged the ward with their blessings. They secretly slipped sweets to their children that often did them no good. I found the visiting hours rather tiresome. I withdrew to my room with Grimm's fairy-tales and read "Table, lay thyself". One visiting day Sister Klara came into my room.

"You've got a visitor."

"Who, me?"

"Yes," she said, looking about the room. "What a nice room you have! A studio all to yourself! How do you spend your time? Is the sister nice to you?"

Only now did I begin to understand her joke. We both laughed.

"I've brought you something."

She produced an envelope from behind her back.

"Go on, open it," she urged.

Awkwardly, I undid the flowery wrapping paper. Out came a box of coloured pencils and a painting-book with alpine flowers. In my joy I forgot to say thank you. The flowers awakened memories in me. I smiled at her.

"Are you satisfied with your visitor?" she teased.

I jumped up from my chair and embraced her, very clumsily, as it turned out. She had to straighten her starched cap. But she had returned my hug. I was happy. Since I had been unable to take my mother in my arms, I had built up a backlog of tenderness.

Sister Klara knew how dangerous it was for a sister to overstep the usual nursing contacts. Patients were only too fond of gossiping about every trifle with their room-mates. Imagination added its embellishments, and "experiences" were sometimes conjured from thin air. This could cause unpleasantness, as morality was writ large in the children's hospital. Personal attachments had to be suppressed. Sister Ida rould tell a tale about that.

She had had to massage a pupil's legs. As you know, the legs include the thighs. Which takes us very close to the heart of the matter. This precocious youth's voice had hardly broken, but he thought his croaking sounds irresistibly masculine. Whether this was actually so or just his fervent wish need not concern us. The young man boasted that while massaging his thighs, the nurse had taken hold of something that lay beyond the call of duty. This caused a big stir. Before long it came to the matron's ears. Sister Ida insisted at great length that she had not been aware of being too familiar with the patient. She could in all honesty swear her innocence as she had been sitting on a chair beside the bed while she massaged. But Sister Ida was assigned to a ward of young children. She had been humiliated, and Christian morality vindicated.

The after-effects of the narcosis and the painkilling injections were having a curious effect on me. Confined to bed for a time after the operation, I tried to embrace Sister Klara at every opportunity. When she shook my pillows, took my pulse, offered me tea or washed my face, I tried to get hold of her. She managed to turn it into a game without hurting my feelings by her caution.

During the day she pushed my bed out onto the veranda. The blinds fanned dazzling yellow light onto the blankets and autumn freshness into my face. I feared the daily visits of the senior doctor. He was always brash when the consultant was not there.

"How's our little Billy-Goat Gruff?" he asked, looking at the sister. She stood beside him, smiling and returning his steady look. It annoyed me to be called that. Nor did I find it quite proper for Sister Klara to smile so amiably at him. The day after the operation he had said:

"You've had a sound sleep. We could hardly get you to wake up. I hope you dreamed about something nice."

I had in fact dreamt of something very curious. I had seen our house in Zumsee. A strange little goblin had flitted about my dream.

"Your father has telephoned," the doctor went on.

"My father? He's phoned?"

"Just before midday. I told him it all went well... Yes... He sends his greetings."

"But... how did he know that...?"

Not noticing that I had something on my mind, the doctor turned to the next patient. As loudly as my voice allowed I called him back to my bed.

"Doctor..."

"Well, what is it?" "Doctor... can I... can I go home soon?"

"Did you hear that, Sister? Hardly has he woken up, and already he wants to leave us. First your wounds have to heal. Or do you think we could let you go home with that dressing on you?"

"But when the wounds have healed? Can I go home then?"
"When the wounds have healed, you may well see things differently. You'll be glad to be rid of that nasty infection, and you might want to stay a few more days with us."
"No. I don't want to stay. I want to go home."
"Fine. I can understand that. But you'll have to be patient with us for a few more days. You'll do that, won't you? When we reach that point, we'll find an answer for you."
"I don't need an answer. I want to go home."
"And we don't want to keep you here any longer than is absolutely necessary!" He turned to the next patient. I did not like these evasive answers at all.

The message

In his long life my father made only two telephone calls. He disliked talking to someone that he could not look in the eye. So he preferred writing letters, even if he had to wait for an answer or an answer never came.

I therefore wondered why he had phoned the hospital. In my letter to my parents I had said nothing about the imminent operation. I didn't want Mother to worry. It was only a week later that I found out from Father why he had phoned. And I was disturbed to find peculiar connections between the contents of his letter and my dream under anaesthetic. If you had asked the old people of Aroleid for their opinion, they would have confirmed that that boded ill, and meaningfully nodded their heads.

According to one of the old beliefs about spirits, a Christian often gave a sign to his family before departing this life. This could happen in enigmatic ways. His soul or spirit would send an unmistakable message. A favourite way of "getting in touch" was to stop the clock in the house concerned. Or to cause such dreadful cracking noises in the timbers that the occupants jumped out of their skins, made the sign of the cross and stared at each other. They guessed at once who was noisily packing his worldly goods. The sender of the message was usually someone struck by illness. But he himself would always find someone else who looked ripe for the long journey. Thus the message always applied to someone else, which was very comforting.

Things became more complicated when the victim of a climbing accident made the announcement in advance. In this case there were no prior signs of illness or weakness. The oracle was far harder to interpret. When the worst happened, those who had been "warned" would clap their hands to their brows. "No wonder – you should have heard the trampling of climbing boots in the attic", they would say. Or: "It was terrible, the wailing in the alley that night."

In my drugged sleep I met a small, extremely nimble little fellow with an enormous mallet of the kind used by carpenters at home for hammering beams together. The midget gave me a brief, spiky little look, guessed my thoughts at once and dashed off at unbelievable speed to give the desired object a blow with the mallet. With a somewhat monotonous rhythm he hit pans, lids and sheet metal objects, creating a monstrous din. Was it my own heartbeats that were becoming audible? Or were all those beliefs about ghosts more than mere fantasy?

In the noisy confusion of my dream I suddenly saw at a great distance a corner of our house in Zumsee. A fine rain was drizzling on to the slate slabs of the roof, then falling to earth in big drops. Straight away, the manikin tore off in that direction. He ran towards the house at extraordinary speed. I could hardly see him, so far off was he. Then he hit the corner of the house with his mallet. I could hear the blow distinctly. Then the little man was back with me, ready to guess my next wish. My father's letter contained an amazing piece of news:

> "Last Tuesday your Mother was busy ironing at our house in Zumsee. Suddenly there was a crash at the corner of the house, at if someone had hit it with a sledgehammer. Mother had a dreadful shock.
> 'Jesus, something's happened to Hannes!' she cried. I had to rush straight down to Zermatt to phone the hospital. You can imagine how relieved I was when the doctor said you had been operated on and were all right. Probably the wall of the house settling under the weight of the slate roof had caused the terrible noise. But it's peculiar that this happened just while you were being operated on."

234

"So that's what it is," I thought. "I've sent a 'message' to my mother. That must mean something. I'm in hospital for a reason!"

As I brooded over this, I received some visitors. Frau Bundesrat and her lively daughter came to see me. They brought grapes, books and a fine picture of the Stafelalp. Behind the old huts and the gnarled pines, the mighty north face of the Horn towered into the blue sky. Cumulus was swirling out from behind the Zmuttgrat. That was how I saw the mountain when I was tending my animals. Immersed in the picture, I forgot to thank them for all the presents. I hardly heard the lady asking the usual questions about how I was. She spoke a homely Berne dialect with a French accent. When she asked:

"Is the sister nice to you?" I nodded with a transparent smile.

"You know, Hannes, we talk a lot about you," she said. "It was so funny on the journey to Berne, how you stood the whole time at the window gazing out. And the way you stared when we took a real taxi to our house! Do you remember? We gave you mineral water, not realising that you only drink well water!" She laughed, trying to cheer me up. "And then the polenta. You didn't like our Riz Casimir. So the cook made a good polenta and you were satisfied." Her kindness was infectious.

"Yes. And Miss Nelly did not want me to fiddle with my fork under the table when I had to say something."

"Aha, you still remember. Good!" said the daughter.

The lady added: "Of course the fork belongs on the table. You know that without Nelly having to tell you, don't you?" and she laughed in her kind, motherly way.

"You must come to see us again soon."

"I'd rather go home. But..."

"But what?"

"... I've... sent a 'message'."

"What have you done?" The ladies looked at each other.

"Sent a message."

They looked at me uncomprehendingly. I grew embarrassed. I said nothing. They couldn't understand it anyway. They were Protestants. Like Sister Klara. Unbelievers. They have nothing to do with ghosts and saints and things like that. They can't even pray in Latin. And that's so important. Perhaps they don't actually believe a person sends a message before he dies. Or that dead people run around atoning for their sins. We all know how unbelieving city folk is.

"You want to go home. I can understand that. But what does the doctor say? Professor Matti told us that, sadly, he couldn't do all that he needed to. You want to be able to use your arm properly again, don't you? He wants to help you some more. That's why we have to be patient, don't we?"

She said it in such a quiet, motherly way that I couldn't disagree. But I felt as if I and my bed were sinking into the depths; I started to cry. The women tried to comfort me.

After a few days the doctor removed the metal clips from the wounds. In two places they were held open with gauze pads to let the last discharge from the infection escape. I now only needed small dressings and was allowed to get up. As soon as I had my feet on the ground again, Sister Klara sent me into the garden.

"You must get some exercise. Then you'll get better more quickly."

Between the ornamental trees and the hazel bushes I saw again the wonderland of the orchard. Red and gold apples, juicy pears and indigo plums crammed the branches. It was like glimpsing the land of milk and honey. In Aroleid there were bilberries, raspberries and small wild strawberries. But fruit trees were unknown in our region. My mouth watered. To sink my teeth into a single pear would have been worth a thrashing from the gardener. But between the pears and me stood Sister Klara. She had advised me not to be caught again. I did not want to disappoint her.

I crept around the hospital cellars, putting my head into all the windows and hatches. There was a opening in the wall with a small hinged grating that could only be reached from the window sill. I had to stand on tiptoe to look into the room. What I saw gave me such a shock that I almost fell.

Before me on a table lay the dead body of a young girl. She was wearing a white hospital smock. Her blond hair hung partly down from the table. In her clasped hands she held some big marguerites. She looked like one of the "White Girls" in the procession at Corpus Christi. Had the nurse put the flowers into her hands? But the room was a bleak cellar. In some places the walls were discoloured by damp. I was deeply shaken.

"She's hidden in a cellar, like cabbage and beetroot. So that no-one knows that someone has croaked. Lucky that I found out. I'll have to tell my room-mates. This will give them something to think about."

And it did.

"What, in the cellar?"

"Whew! That's cruel."

"Yes. And it's dark down there."

"Ugh! And what happens if mice come?"

"I'll tell my father."

"They've got a nerve!"

Sister Klara, too, was surprised when she heard my story. "Do you have to get up to mischief every time I send you into the garden? Why don't you come to me first when you discover something new? You've got my children into a fine state. I'm really disappointed with you!" And she withdrew her affection for two whole days and put me on the meagre, impersonal diet of the hospital patients. I realised that someone who talked big could never be her friend.

Night duty

When everyone else in the world is still asleep, the patients in hospitals are already being roused so that they can experience the early-morning thermometer ceremony in full consciousness. It is accompanied by the taking of the pulse and the plotting of temperature curves on the graph paper that adorns the head or foot of each bed. The doctor needs these data so that he can glance at them on his daily rounds and say "Oho" or "Aha" to cover his confusion. One day in hospital resembles another like two drops of water. Unless, of course, there is an exceptional change of menu and you are given apple puree with pudding instead of pudding with apple puree.

The weekly visits by the consultant vary the routine. The nurses nervously check each wrinkle in the sheets. They smile encouragement to the patients, quickly empty a last bed pan and, reflected in the mirror-polished linoleum floor, await the arrival of the white gods – the consultant with his comet's tail of senior and junior doctors, matrons and nurses. Like a kite he sweeps with his train through the many rooms and wards. If he stops by a bed, that patient's fate takes a dramatic new turn. He will either go up the ladder, or down. The invalid anxiously tries to glean one or two Latin phrases, which are of no help to him. At most they allow him to guess why and when he will next come under the knife. He appeals in alarm to the attending nurse, who replies:

"Search me! I know nothing. You'd better ask the doctor, but he's sure not to tell you much either."

I trembled each time the consultant's visit drew near. Standing at the foot of the bed, I awaited the fateful, white-clad procession and submitted myself to it in utter passivity. And that was just as well. I should never have had the courage to agree to all they had in store for me.

In the first operation all the inflamed areas of bone were drained. The long scar from wrist to elbow on the inside of the arm and the nine-centimetre-long scar on the outside of the arm remained as a sign of hard work.

In the second operation there was talk of tendon grafts. They wanted to sew the tendons controlling the movement of the wrist to the finger tendons to give mobility to the fingers. This operation was a failure. But my inability to hold a glass of water after the operation did not discourage the doctors. On the contrary, it only increased their determination.

"All that remains is to fix the thumb. It must be re-aligned in relation to the index finger. So that this useless hand can at least perform simple tasks, such as holding a cup. I could not imagine how this was to be managed. All I knew was that the nurse had to "prepare" me again.

One must give the doctors credit for the fact that between the various operations they give the patient the chance to recuperate physically and sometimes even mentally. But because the days are so alike, the weeks fly past and you are amazed that it's already time for the next operation.

To keep me occupied, Sister Klara entrusted a few tasks to me. I was allowed to polish the floor, distribute the meals, feed some of the helpless patients, empty urine bottles and comfort small children when their mothers had gone home on visiting days. Three times a week an elderly Swedish masseuse massaged my arm, and three times I had to put it in an incubator to loosen what tissue and muscle was left. I was turning into a well-trained long-term patient and getting used to the white hospital rooms.

Unfortunately, Sister Klara had to take overnight duty on our ward. This duty was rotated among the nurses in a three-monthly cycle. Sister Martha took over the patients in rooms 26 and 27. She was strict and humourless. From the start I fell foul of her pedantic ways. She tried to teach me that you had to eat whatever was put on your plate. Including things you didn't like. That is, including spinach.

At three in the afternoon I was still at table, contemplating a full plate of cold spinach. I had an aversion to all vegetables, but spinach was the worst. Especially when finely chopped. It produced in me an inclination to vomit. Once I had actually done so. But that had not impressed Sister Martha.

"Anyone who cannot eat spinach will never turn out well!" She cleared away all the other plates and dishes.

"You'll get something else when you've finished the spinach. Is that clear?"

It was clear. But I had long since given up trying to eat the greenish-grey mess with the white specks. I sat at the table, distraughtly swinging my legs. The sister had staked her whole authority on the spinach and was bent on asserting her inviolable will.

Unluckily for her, the senior doctor was doing his afternoon round. Surprised at my slow eating habits, he asked the sister to follow him into the corridor. Thereupon the plate was removed, and I never again had to touch spinach. I kept this up in later life. Perhaps that's why I never turned out well. On this point I have to defer to Sister Martha. But the realisation has come very late. Too late for me to acquire a taste for spinach.

The spinach puree had a sequel. Sister Martha complained to the night sister about the cheeky boy with the extraordinary eating habits.

"Heaven knows what people eat up in those mountains. He won't even eat chopped spinach. It could drive a person to distraction!"

That night, Sister Klara woke me from my midnight sleep. "I've heard you wouldn't eat your spinach today," she said. "You're driving us to distraction. There! Show us you can empty your plate."

She put a tray in front of me. I rubbed my eyes, yawned heartily and sat up. It must have been midnight. On my lap was a big plate of crisp fried potatoes with chopped veal in sour cream sauce. I couldn't believe my eyes. And I showed Sister Klara that I could empty my plate!

"You have to build your strength up," she said. I showed her I was doing that as well. Embracing her, I pressed her so hard against me that she couldn't breathe.

She sat on my bed. She had pushed up the sleeves of her spotted dress. I stroked her long, bare arms. Now and then she sighed. We kissed each other on the mouth. Her breast was so close to my fingers that I wanted to touch it with my cupped hand, as the men at home did with such aplomb. But I had inhibitions. I thought I might upset Sister Klara. She might find it unpleasant. She would slap me on the hand and say: "That still belongs to me," as our girls used to do. We both sighed and hugged each other like big children.

It was winter. Damp and cold. There was mist outside the windows for days on end. The lamp in my room burned almost continuously. The trees stretched their leafless branches towards the sky. They, too, could not reach the sun. The puffing of the trains at the station was hardly audible. But no snow had fallen yet.

I had read Grimm's Fairytales twice over. I could hardly tell what was enchanted and what was not. But I knew one thing: my valley must now be enchanted by winter. I saw a landscape in deep snow. From people's mouths came pennants of breath. The snow crunched under their feet. The sky was clear and blue, the sun blinding. School must have started long ago. My schoolmates were fetching their boards from the sheds and careering down the valley. This, too, had become a part of Grimm's Fairytales.

I was mad on ski-jumping. Once, just before the jumping competition, we boys had built a small ramp. From it you could jump 18 metres. But on one attempt I landed beyond the packed surface. I dug into the snow and badly damaged my knee. That evening Mother helped me hide the injury from Father to spare me a telling-off. But the next day the knee was badly swollen. I couldn't bend it, and we had to call the doctor. By the day of the school jumping competition, the knee had not healed. But I got on my father's nerves so much with my whining and complaining that he finally let me take part.

In those days we did not have special skis for jumping. We had to show our prowess with simple planks with leather straps and metal strips at the sides. Style was not assessed, just distance. With my injured knee, I jumped very stiffly. Fearing the pain of landing, I turned up my toes. This pulled the skis up and made me lean backwards. Only by windmilling with my arms was I able to land on my feet. No wonder I was not among the leaders. None of my jumps came near the 30 metre limit.

At the beginning of February I was to have my third operation. This impressed even my friends in Berne. "A short break in your hospital life would do you good," the lady comforted me. "We'll talk to the consultant and then you'll come to stay with us for a week in the holidays. Would you like that?"

I actually was allowed to go in my Sunday suit and some of my underwear to Sulganau Street. At first I moved shyly among the many rooms of the large villa, but I soon began to feel at home. The head of the household had by now become president of our country and the servants and postmen talked of him with respect. Unfortunately, I wasn't allowed to eat with the servants. The family wanted me to sit with them at table. The lack of refined manners I displayed while eating did not deter them from having me at table with the guests in the evening as well. Often an extra course was served for me, such as fried polenta slices or crisp baked macaroni mixed with egg and cheese, my favourite dishes. I could not understand how people could eat eels or shrimps or other sea creatures that looked like snakes, maggots or spiders. The father of the family would tease me about this:

Hans, Hans, the mountain boy has all that he could want. But what he wants he does not have.

And what he has he does not want. Hans, Hans, the mountain boy has all that he could want.

I stood up for myself: "I've got my polenta, and I don't want anything else. Your crab will pinch you on the nose." He laughed and said: "Enjoy your polenta. It's healthier."

I encountered city life, was amazed by the many trams that came and went and always found the right rails. I saw the bears in front of the History Museum, whose tongues the sculptor had forgotten to carve, was shocked by the "Ogre" fountain and admired the self-assurance of Mother Helvetia on the monument to the World Postal Union as she passed the Swiss post on to the other nations clinging grimly to the globe. I was pleased to see that the bears ate sugar beet in their pit, and asked if you could throw them spinach as well.

Miss Nelly took me to see *Peter's Flight to the Moon* at the City Theatre. It was a stirring fairy-tale. Peter had to fetch the maybug's lost leg from the moon. The Man in the Moon made difficulties, and he had many other obstacles to overcome. Perhaps I was so entranced by the story because I had found a fellow-sufferer in the maybug. I too had lost a limb, that I hoped to find again at the hospital.

On the last day of the holiday the sun shone again – it was like a spring day. Nelly explained that this was the effect of the Foehn. Today we would have a good view of the mountains, she said.

"I'd so like to see the mountains," I begged.

Miss Nelly agreed to accompany me to the terrace of the Parliament buildings. When we were in the tram, she changed her mind. "We'll go up the minster tower. There you'll have as good a view as if you were on a mountain."

We climbed three-hundred steps to the viewing balcony. We were received by what I took to be a hut-keeper. "He's not a hut-keeper," said Nelly, "he's the tower warden. Something like a fireman." When he heard I came from Zermatt, he told us he'd drunk some milk on the Stafelalp. And of course he had seen the Kalbermatte. There had been some cows grazing on it.

"How small the world is," I thought.

He showed us his little living-room. An old grandfather clock ticked noisily. He told us how the tower swayed slightly when the wind gusted across the country.

From the balcony that ran right round the tower I looked on to a sea of roofs and chimneys. The River Aare had cut elaborate curls and loops in the landscape. Here and there the water glittered. Large bridges spanned the cuttings. I knew their names from my geography lessons. Miss Nelly was surprised. "We mountain folk are not as ignorant as you think," I teased her.

On the southern margin of the sky stood the mountains. A garland of points, peaks and domes. Each jagged line clearly visible. The whole chain of Alps in deep snow. Above it a sky with long banks of cloud like endless furrows.

I couldn't look at it long enough. Homesickness began to prickle beneath my shirt. Miss Nelly moved away, leaving me a moment on my own. I could look across to the mountains, now and then passing my coat sleeve across my nose, without being ashamed.

The next day I went back to the hospital.

The surprise

Problems awaited me there. I had to vacate my single room to a newly-operated patient and move into the large ward. Sister Klara was still on night duty. On her nightly rounds she could no longer sit on the edge of my bed. One patient or another was always awake, and our whispering would have attracted attention. Our untroubled trysts were over. Shortly before Sister Klara went off duty in the early morning, she came into our ward to tell Sister Martha about a patient who had vomited in the night. I was sitting at the big table, painting a winter landscape with water colours. A path led past some pines to a hut. "What a lot of snow there is on that roof," said Sister Klara as she passed. In a low voice she added: "You ought to give your shoes another clean. Now."

Obtusely, I answered: "They don't need it."

"Are you such a dimwit?" she asked, hardly audibly, bending over the painting, and left.

"Aha," I murmured inadvertently. No-one had noticed this little exchange. I waited a moment then slipped out of the room. Down in the basement, in the shoe-cleaning room, Sister Klara was waiting. Shoes and brushes had been put out for the benefit of unforeseen visitors. She made fun of my slow wits. I should have known what she had meant by coming into the ward.

"Some people have a thick skull," she laughed.

"I can't read thoughts," I countered.

"Well, you ought to. Now we have known each other so long." But then she suddenly grew serious. "I think you'll be sent home soon. I'll miss you."

"Why? Have you heard something?"

Nurses don't like passing on things they have overheard from doctors. They can burn their fingers too easily. Her dark eyes shone below her brows, which almost joined in the middle. Her gaze rested on me.

"I need to know," I went on. "They haven't finished patching up my arm."

She lowered her eyes. I wanted to take her in my arms, but a door closed nearby. We heard steps. Sister Klara grabbed her brush and shoes. I bent over mine. The gardener trudged along the corridor in his rubber boots. He went past our door. We laughed awkwardly and comforted each other in our relief, but Sister Klara's thoughts were elsewhere. She tried to smile, but her eyes were far from happy.

At lunchtime I was spooning gruel into little Carlo while his exotic eyes looked at me in gratitude. I liked this little fellow, who lay in a plaster cast that badly hampered his movements. For some time I had felt I was being watched. As I became conscious of it, I looked round to the door. I could hardly believe my eyes! Father was standing in the open doorway with the matron. They had been watching me.

Almost dropping the plate, I ran up to him. He grabbed the doorframe, otherwise I should have bowled him over. It was my father, beyond any doubt! It smelt of him. Of strong tobacco and sour-sweet clothes. He was there to take me home. Father was very anxious to talk to the consultant. That was why he had made the long journey, the matron told me.

Professor Matti received us in his private office. Like all leading surgeons, he was tight-lipped and nervous. At each question you asked you felt you were stealing his time. And his time seemed to be in short supply. He tried to answer my father courteously: "I haven't much to tell you. We've done what could be done. I'm afraid that's how it is. In the last operation we gave the hand some ability to grip. We fixed the thumb to bring it into contact with the forefinger. That was successful. Now the boy can wedge a glass of water between his finger and thumb."

Father tried to say something.

"Take your time," said the professor.

Father nodded. He found his voice again.

"Do you... do you think I can make Dr. Hörnli responsible? I mean legally?"

"That won't be easy. The harmful effect of the plaster is clear. I agree with you about that. And I'm willing to confirm it. But the court will need proof that a malpractice has been committed or that the doctor has been guilty of gross negligence."

"So he has!"

"It looks like it. But that's a matter of judgement. The other party will contest it. Who can prove it?"

"You, Professor! You can!"

"No, I can't. I can only confirm that there has been a compression caused by the plaster, which has led to the damage."

"But that's just the point."

"I can't prove the malpractice. I'm sorry."

"You only need to look at the arm. It's obvious!"

"That may be enough for us, but not for the lawyers. They're contentious people. That's the situation. I'm sorry."

Father had grown very thoughtful. He thanked the surgeon, and we left.

Father carried my little case as we walked down a long avenue of trees. He put his left hand on my shoulder. It was the hand with the missing fingers. The Indian woman who had looked after him after the amputation in Yungay had buried them, with his right foot. "So they can rise again with the other limbs on the Day of Judgement" she told him. But until the Day of Judgement, one had to manage without them.

The wind rustled the leaves of the plane trees. Father bent his head to stop it lifting his hat. He stopped, put down the case and pulled the hat lower. I wanted to carry the case. He stopped me: "Leave it. I'll take it. We've both got the same problem." Apart from that he did not say much. This suited me, for I was brooding on what the surgeon had said. I had had some doubts earlier, but had always driven them away. Now I felt something coming towards me that I could no longer escape. I was afraid.

We passed the first tram stop without paying it any attention. We walked towards the town. At the second stop we waited for the no. 1 tram that was to take us to the station. "We'll thank our friends in Berne on the way back. I don't want to go there today. They might think we're ungrateful."

I didn't understand him, but I nodded. He looked very tired. "You would like to visit your brother in Luthern, wouldn't you?"

"Yes, I haven't seen him for a long time."

"We'll go as far as Wolhusen today. We'll be picked up there tomorrow. His boss has a small van."

The journey

In Visp we took the horse-drawn post coach. The small covered compartment had room for four people. On a rather bumpy road we reached Stalden. Here, there was only a mule path winding erratically along the southern slope of the valley. Up and down it went, skirting the rocky outcrops. Father preferred to walk along the track of the valley railway, with the case in his hand. In the shady crevices and tunnel entrances, arm-thick icicles still hung. At lunch in Sankt Niklaus we met Theodor Kronig, who transported letters and parcels along the valley in a little mule-cart. Here the road was better. Kronig was a friendly coachman who liked to tease. He loaded our case on to the cart and for some of the time let us ride on it. When the road climbed, we walked beside the cart. He told us that our Karolina, who had helped us one summer on our pasture at Kalbermatten, had married a few weeks before. He had heard it from a man in Törbel.

As we drew nearer to Zermatt, I grew quieter and quieter. I was thinking about how I would face the people of the village. I was known as a daredevil. Far too ambitious for the meagre talents nature had endowed me with. I always wanted to be first. Now I was coming home with clipped wings, with no chance of soaring to the heights, hardly good enough for the back row, no longer a proper mountain boy. The barmaid at the Gasthof zur Sonne at Luthern had summed it up. We had gone there with my brother for a glass of wine. Alfons seemed on good terms with her. "This is my younger brother," he said. "The one with the arm." The barmaid looked me over and said: "Pity about the lad. What's going to happen when he wants to get married?" This was new to me. I had not yet dared think that far ahead. But she was right. What would happen if I wanted to marry one day?

We were in the lane leading to our village. Since the accident people had always taken an interest in me. They would ask how my arm is. And I would have to tell them I've become a cripple. That was humiliating. Father watched me for a time, then he asked:
"What's the matter with you? Do you feel sick?"
"No."
He looked at me doubtfully. I repeated somewhat more loudly: "No!"
"You've gone quite pale. Aren't you happy to be coming home?"
"Yes, I am."
"Why are you so quiet? Is something wrong?"
"No."
After a moment he said:
"I understand, my boy. I didn't find it easy to go back home either when I came back from Yangay. I could hardly stand."
I nodded.
"It takes time."
"It's not that."
"You mean the people? The people here are kind."
"I know."
"They like you. They'll be sorry for you."
"I don't need pity!" I had said it too fiercely.
"No. Of course not. But the people are all right. No-one in our village has ever tried to take another's life. Never!"
I looked at Father in surprise. Why did he say that? Did he think I could do anything so stupid? He'd said himself that he could murder the bloody doctor. You say things like that, but you don't do them.
The previous night I had had a strange dream. I was rummaging in our attic for dynamite and fuses. Suddenly an old man with a shotgun came out of the gun box. He held the weapon out to me and said: "Go on, you duffer, show him!" My legs were like lead; try as I might, I could

not move from the spot. When the old man grabbed my shoulder, I woke up. My forehead was damp. I threw the heavy blanket on the floor but could not get back to sleep. Confused thoughts tormented me. Now in broad daylight I was amazed that I could have thought such things. "It takes time", Father sighed once more.

At the entrance to the village, the cart stopped by the post office. Kronig would not accept any money. We thanked him. Father took the little case and we went up the village street. I was annoyed that he did not choose the back way behind the hotels. There we would have met hardly anybody. Perhaps Father did not want that to happen. Perhaps he wanted me to face my fate. He strolled along at a leisurely pace, limping slightly because of his frostbitten food. I walked beside him.

We met a lot of people. They greeted us affably and asked about my arm. I found it hard to tell them what the position was. I never found the way from the station to our house so long. I was glad when we finally reached our flat and I could take my mother in my arms.

Father had decided to get compensation from the doctor for the incorrect treatment.

"For that I need a competent lawyer. Not one from Upper Valais. Those learned fools all know each other. They're all in it together. I need one from Lower Valais."

And he found one. Now he had to go frequently to Visp for court hearings. He was in good heart. When he had stopped for a glass of wine on the way back, he was especially confident.

"It's going well. You should have seen how our lawyer banged the table with his fist. The judge just stared," he laughed.

And the case went on.

The village priest was a close friend of our doctor. That's why I didn't seek him out at the presbytery, although it was usual for a stray sheep who had been away from home for some time to pay him a visit. I met him by chance one day in the square in front of the church. He did not seem particularly pleased.

"Can I see your arm?" he asked.

It embarrassed me to roll up my sleeve and show my arm in the village square, with people standing around. I normally kept my hand hidden in my trouser pocket. Father Bittel glanced at the skin-covered bones, from which the tissue and muscle were missing, and asked in a jocular tone:

"Have the mice been at it?"

I could not utter a word. But the man of God met my eyes, which told him how much he had hurt me. Red-faced, I turned away from him and walked homewards. I took just one sombre look back. In his long cassock, with only his soles and heels showing beneath it, he was striding with Christian dignity towards the presbytery.

In court we were able to prove that Dr. Hörnli had lied on an important matter. He had asserted that on the day of my accident he had called unbidden at our house and had observed nothing unusual. We had witnesses to testify that we had had to call the doctor three or four hours after the accident because of the pain I was in. They testified that by that time my fingers were cold and dark blue and that I had vomited several times. So the case was going well. Father was already counting on 5000 francs for injuries suffered, 20 000 francs sickness compensation and 10 000 francs indemnity for the family. "You'll be able to get a proper training. I promise you that. Then you'll make your way in the world."

But the trial dragged on. The court called for expert medical opinion. And counter-opinion. The doctors wrote lengthy epistles and treatises, quoting their white gods and sacred cows. And the lawyers were at each other's throats. Then came a letter from our solicilor. He mentioned that the court had received an important report from Professor

Matti. He could not quote the entire contents, but the most important passage went as follows:

Professor Matti: It is beyond doubt that the alterations I noted in the arm, namely ischaemic muscular contraction, paralysis of the nerves of the forearm and bone necrosis, *were the result of a too severe and prolonged compression of the forearm by the plaster cast.*

The solicitor believed this statement must have a positive influence on the case. He also mentioned a letter from Dr. Hörnli to Professor Matti, in which the doctor had incriminated himself:

Dr. Hörnli: I soon observed that despite the good supervision and the good cotton-wool padding there was an excessive constriction of the arm.

Father was confident that nothing could go wrong now. Professor Matti was, after all, the doctor who had taken me over and treated me in my wretched state. Things looked bad for the other side. So they persuaded the judge to seek further expert opinion and the case went on. Since the fees for the reports from the "leading experts in the field" were extremely high, the lawyers, who were getting nervous about their own fees, tried to agree on a "neutral party". The court awaited their suggestions.

My parents did not want to send me up to the alp in the summer. "We'll look for a job in the village for you."

"Don't you think I'm any good as a shepherd any more?"

"No, it's not that. We have to make sure you get a training. And the judge might send for you."

First I tried the baker. He needed a delivery boy to take loaves and rolls to the hotels and guest houses in a big basket. He would have to be able to ride through the streets and alleys on an old bicycle with a full basket on his back. That was unfortunately beyond me now.

Then I applied to the head office of the Seiler Hotel chain. I asked for the post of "casserollier" at the Hotel Monte Rosa.

"Why casserollier? And why do you specially want the Hotel Monte Rosa?" the director laughed.

"Because I like the work there." I did not say that I had often looked through the back windows of the hotel kitchen. A casserollier polished the magnificent copper pans till they shone like the evening sky. He sang at the top of his voice as he worked. And if a tasty morsel came back on a dish from the dining-room to the kitchen, he plucked it up as it passed.

"I've always thought casserollier was the job for me."

"Don't you think you'd need both hands for the heavy pans?"

"Look," I explained laboriously, "I can wedge the pan handles between my finger and thumb."

"I'm still concerned that it might be too much for you. But that reminds me – we've installed a lift at the Monte Rosa. You could work the lift."

"You mean I could be the lift-boy?"

"Exactly."

"Oh yes, please."

I received my first work contract. This boosted my self-confidence. Joyfully I rushed to the village seamstress to order the uniform on behalf of my employers. From good, forget-me-not-blue cloth she made up a splendid suit with broad stripes along the trouser seams, stand-up collar and gold buttons. I looked like a general's son and henceforth bore the gold inscription "Hotel Monte Rosa" on my breast.

Do unto others...

In the hotels of those days, the hotel employees were caught between two evils. That of the untroubled, easy-going life-style of the guests who, in comfortable surroundings, came to their tables with prodigious appetites, in an expectant glow of anticipation, and that of the nutritive abundance which issued from enchanted kitchens and well-ordered wine cellars to soothe and satisfy the palates of the hotel clients.

These two evils held their brief, seasonal tryst, bringing with them a conflict of interests. Behind the guest's seemingly heedless expenditure lay the desire for more and more luxury, which of course clashed head-on with the hotelier's profit motive, which manifested itself in the opening of Aladdin's cave so far but not further. Between them were the hotel employees, dependent on tips from the one and at the mercy of the powers-that-be in the miniature domain ot the hotel.

They moved about the hotel, like circus performers, in their liveried uniforms, balancing delicious morsels on shining trays, hardly daring even to breathe in the delectable aromas, always at hand, even at the most inconvenient moments, to fulfil the guest's every whim, whether it be a telephone connection to the other side of the world or having a private word with St. Peter concerning the state of the weather.

They took note of the most impossible requests, removed and replenished mountains of bed-linen and personal laundry, whisked away used ashtrays, creased table napkins and crumpled newspapers. In all, they pandered to their guests' every whim, however eccentric, never allowing their solicitous smiles to slip.

Father had bought me Sunday shoes. They shone dully, did not contain a single nail and were so light that I could not help skipping when I had them on my feet. Dressed in my darkblue uniform I stood before my lift like a shimmering dragonfly, waiting for the guests entrusted to my care.

On my first trip the director accompanied me in person.

"Always show the guests a cheerful face," he advised me paternally. "Never turn your back on them. If you have something sensible to say, chat to them. Some of them like that. And never forget: the guest is always king!"

How could I have forgotten this last injunction so quickly? I must have had a memory like a sieve even then. A family which was closely related to a northern royal house was staying at the hotel. They had three sons aged from seven to twelve and occupied a number of rooms on the south side of the third floor, the best position, with a view of the Matterhorn, as was right and proper. The parents were addressed reverently as Count and Countess. When the boys were referred to, one spoke of the "young gentlemen". The hotel employees had spontaneous attacks of spinal curvature whenever they met them in the halls or corridors.

I should have liked to play with the boys, but they spoke a tongue full of impossible sounds quite unlike what was taught in our schools. The Count and Countess had numerous engagements, and the children spent too much time hanging around the hotel rooms and passages. They were bored. No wonder they got the idea of teasing me. They rang for the lift from the third, fourth or fifth floor. When I arrived in my stately conveyance and opened the door, there was no-one to be seen. All I heard was the patter of children's feet running to seek refuge in their rooms. To judge by the laughter and commotion, this game was providing them with huge enjoyment. I found it less diverting.

For a time I continued making the fruitless ascents. Then I lost patience and devised a battle plan. When the lift was yet again summoned from the fourth floor, I admitted the guests on the ground floor and asked them to operate the lift themselves. I then ran up the stairs as fast as I could and met the boisterous lads running downstairs in their slippers, making for their rooms on the third floor. In time-honoured fashion I dealt out punishment to right and left. The exuberant laughter gave way to screams and howls. I thought I had re-established order in our dignified hotel, but I had reckoned without the manageress. I was summoned to the director's office. The worthy old manageress showed me how much vigour she could still muster. She wanted to fire me on the spot. "What in heaven's name were you thinking of? Have you any idea what you've done? You have worse manners than a stable boy. You'll leave the hotel this instant."

But the Countess, who had been present at this one-sided exchange, did not want her to go so far.

"We don't wish to cause trouble for the boy. The Count and I only request that such a thing should not be repeated. He shouldn't lose his position because of it. That would embarrass us."

But the manageress was not so easily placated.

"Thank the Countess for her boundless generosity, you..."

Now I too felt my spine beginning to bend compulsively.

"But he must be punished, Countess. He's got to learn his lesson."

"May I leave that to you?" the Countess asked, and took her leave. The manageress pondered for a while how she could best take her revenge. Then she remembered the long, wrought-iron bannister that the servants always neglected. I was ordered to take a duster to it.

"Not a speck of dust do I want to see – you understand? And this is extra work, to be done outside working hours, every day. Is that understood?"

How could a blacksmith be so stupid as to create such a bannister? It was an endless convolution of scrolls and curls with nooks art crannies everywhere for dust to collect. Even with a wet cloth it was hard to reach. During this extra work I had more than enough time to reflect that the same justice did not operate at the hotel as on the mountain. How fine it was when I could live by the principle: "What you do to me, I can do to you!"

I was surprised to find the incident had earned me the sympathy of the staff. I was regarded as a little hero. Behind a precautionary hand the maids and waitresses would complain about the pranks of the "young gentlemen". They didn't dare call them "rascals" even in a whisper. And they took care not to voice their complaints to the bosses. Only the waitress Hermine, who looked like the sister of the storybook pranksters Max and Moritz, saw fit to say:

"Congratulations! You've finally taught them some manners. A good Swiss thrashing is always the best cure! By the way, do you like roast chicken?"

I did not know what roast chicken had to do with my ruffianly behaviour, but I did not conceal my partiality to such fowl in the roasted state.

"All right. Now listen! Roast chicken is on the menu today. Make sure you stay near the restaurant during dinner. There are always guests who don't like chicken."

"How could the Lord create people who did not like roast chicken?" I wondered. At the appointed time I was standing expectantly near the dining-room. Each time the swing doors to the pantry opened, a wonderful aroma floated from the room where the cooks were working. But it only made my mouth water. Suddenly Hermine was next to me, saying:

"Here! Take it! In the serviette!" And she tripped back into the pantry.

I retreated to the lift with the white napkin. Stopping between the second and third floors, I unrolled from the cloth a crisp leg of roast chicken and consumed it at my leisure. No-one could disturb my enjoyment. If anyone wished to speak to me, they would have to ring. When the Count's family left, the red carpet was rolled out to see them off; many were the bows and curtsies, but the long faces were no fewer. They did not leave behind what the well-wishers had been hoping for. Naturally, I went away empty-handed. The countess's attendant did not want to reward my misdeed. I could understand that. Nor had I expected anything, so I was not disappointed. On the contrary. The three "young gentlemen" came up to me and shook my hand. I did not understand what they said, but I was glad they did not bear me a grudge. That was worth more to me than a couple of francs in my trouser pocket.

It was a lucky day for me all round. Every high point is a springboard for the next. The saying "It never rains but it pours" can apply in reverse. With the Count's family, an English alpinist also left. Mr. Spencer was highly respected in mountaineering circles. He was one of the guests who regarded the Hotel Monte Rosa as their mountain home. He detested the slightest change to the hotel. He loved it as it was, from tradition, as a memorial. Everything ought to stay as it was at the time of "sacred mountaineering". To him, modernisation was sacrilege.

During his whole stay he had not once used the lift. The services I had performed for him could be counted on the fingers of one hand. I had brought the "Times" to the reading-room and emptied the ashtray a few times, when he had knocked out his bent meerschaum pipe. That was all. It was hardly worth a tip. As the porter, the driver, the two upper-floor porters and I stood in line at the entrance as he left, to my surprise he passed me something too. I felt a five-franc piece in my hand. Unbelievable! I had never received such a princely tip. I grabbed his hand, which he was about to put back into his pocket, and pressed it with such fervent gratitude that Mr. Spencer cried out:

"Damn it, you're killing me!" He was laughing, but still rubbing his hand, as he climbed into the waiting horse-drawn omnibus. As befitted a proper lift-boy, I kept the money loose in my trouser pocket. When I felt for it, it gave a silvery clink beneath the cloth.

Hotel Monte Rosa

The builders had placed the Hotel Monte Rosa right against a cliff. Behind it the rocky wall rose far above the roof of the hotel. On that side there were some rooms that had the sheer wall directly outside the window. If you wanted to see the sky, you had to lean right out. As this was not to everybody's taste, these rooms were not popular. The sun only favoured the windows facing east and south. The side facing the rocks was steeped in bluish shadow. When German guests arrived, they usually marched straight to the window, threw it open and descended fuming to see the manager. Swiss married couples looked helplessly at each other when they saw the "view", and pursed their lips. They only expressed their disappointment when they were alone in the room. On the other hand, the proximity of the cliff did not seem to matter to the English. They paid no attention to it. They were in the hotel where Whymper, Lord Douglas and so many other famous mountaineers had stayed – and that was enough for them. As if it was all just as they had imagined it, they tipped the baggage porter and said: "All right". Let me make it clear that there were only a few rooms that faced the cliff. I hope this will be understood, as I should like to be able to walk past the hotel in my latter years without some stray flower pot, dislodged from a window-sill by who knows what fickle wind, landing on my head.

The English would often ask me if they should appear in a dinner jacket at the "table d'hôte" in the evening. Although most of the guests usually dined in ordinary suits, I advised them to put on full evening dress, since I enjoyed seeing people in their formal regalia.

Since my contretemps with the count's sons I had had to start work regularly before breakfast. With my bucket and duster I toiled at the convoluted bannister. Although I was sometimes more asleep than awake as I worked, I must have softened the manageress's heart. One morning I felt a hand on my shoulder as I knelt yet again before the ironmongery. The manageress stood behind me.

"Let it be now," she said kindly. "You don't need to do this work any more. Go and get your breakfast."

I almost dropped the bucket of water on her feet in my eagerness to comply.

I had gradually got the hang of the lift-boy's complex tasks. With the celebrated service to the guest you could easily go too far. Feathers would fly if you usurped the task of a superior. But operating the lift alone was not enough to bring in a good supply of tips. It was the small, additional services that counted. This gave me the most disgraceful ideas. I hid the "Manchester Guardian", the "Times", the "Frankfurter Allgemeine" and the "Neue Zürcher Zeitung" in the billiards room. Then, when I noticed a guest looking for a paper, I quickly fetched the appropriate journal, adding to my tally of points at the farewell tipping performance.

My trick with the letter post unfailingly brought me favour. The concierge watched over the newly-arrived post like a spider guarding its prey. It would have amounted to a criminal act had I handed out the letters from the pigeonholes. But I noted which slots contained letters, and when the guests concerned took the lift down to the restaurant, I apprised them of the waiting mail.

After dinner there was often an opportunity to push a number of armchairs together. You had to be able to guess which guests preferred to sit alone and which wanted to be together.

I earned less credit when I rushed to the swing doors at the entrance, whisked them open in front of a guest's nose and then slammed them in the face of the next, because people were already waiting to get into the lift. You could not be everywhere at once. There was no reward for emptying ashtrays. And if you kept breaking matches in your eagerness to light someone's cigarette while the guest in question irritably twirled his lighter in his hand, your credit dropped still further.

A good hotel employee avoided talking about the weather when it was raining cats and dogs outside. But when the barometer rose a degree or two I would make my way along the halls like a prophet proclaiming the forthcoming change in the weather.

"Tu morrou weri gud wedder egein."

I picked up these fragments of English during the meals. The concierge and the porter, with whom I sat at table, amused themselves by teaching me new expressions. They taught me that "Go to hell" meant "Have a pleasant journey." But you only wished people a pleasant journey if you did not want to see them again. So different were the customs in England.

From then on I wished all the guests who did not tip me a pleasant journey. Luckily they either did not hear or could not understand my English.

For a time we had an English clergyman at the hotel. He must have been a high dignitary, since he arrived with three ladies in attendance. They occupied different rooms. The man of the cloth was very popular with the guests, who stood around him in swarms whenever he showed himself.

To my horror I noticed that the reverend gentleman frequently emerged from the room of one or other of the ladies in the morning. That is to say, a chambermaid had first drawn my attention to the fact. I now acquired Sherlock Holmes-like powers of observation. And indeed, my suspicions were confirmed. I decided to put a stop to the goings-on on the third floor, and wondered whether I should myself accost the sinner or leave it to the management. Luckily I decided on the latter course, since it gave me an opportunity to demonstrate my gratitude to the manageress.

The hotel doyenne, who had listened to my opening remark without a word, let me describe my observations at length. But she showed no shock at the state of affairs on the third floor. On the contrary, she simply smiled and advised me to abstain from such observations in future. Very often guests were related, or had to lend each other something. A visit in pyjamas to another room, even if it lasted longer that we might think necessary, was nothing wicked and no reason to get excited. People knew what they were doing. I should just keep my attention on my lift and serve the guests politely, then all would be well. She showed me out with a benevolent smile.

The supreme expert

"When you arrive in Basle," my father advised, "take a taxi and show the driver this piece of paper. Then he'll know where to take you. I've always done that in strange towns."

"Where will I find a taxi?"

"They always stand in front of the station entrance."

As I got off the train in Basle, I asked another passenger where the station entrance was.

"Just follow you nose like everybody else," he replied curtly.

I stood on the platform and looked around me. There was indeed only one way out of the station.

It was midday. At two o'clock I had to report to a professor in the Birmannsgasse; he was to provide the final expert opinion on my arm, since the previous medical experts had not reached unanimity on the question of guilt. My father did not agree with this procedure:

"The little people have to appear in court and swear before God and the saints to tell the truth. But we have to go to see the Herr Professor in his private rooms. No-one puts him under oath! He's too high and mighty" – thus he remonstrated.

Mother had given me a paper bag with a rye-bread and cheese sandwich. I had no time to eat the sandwich in the train, as I had to change in Visp, Brig, Berne and Olten. That required my undivided attention. As I still had two hours to spare, I sat down on a bench under a lilac bush in a nearby park and devoured my sandwich while people scurried around nervously on the tramway island.

I went back in good time to the station entrance and knocked on the window of one of the cars standing there. The driver gave me an unfriendly look and opened the door. I gave him the paper. "What am I supposed to do with this?" he asked.

"Drive me there."

He shook his head. "Who do you think I am. Pestalozzi? I'm not even a taxi driver." He gave me back the paper and slammed his door. A newspaper vendor was standing nearby. He had overheard the conversation. With his whole portable kiosk he accompanied me to the nearby taxi stand. Sometimes he stopped, since he wanted to know why I had come to Basle and what business I had in the Birmannsgasse. I therefore felt obliged to tell the whole story to the taxi driver as well, the newspaper vendor confirming what I said.

I got into the taxi, and waved to the newspaper vendor through the back window. We criss-crossed a large number of streets. I think the taxi-driver himself was surprised to find the Birmannsgasse in the medley of alleys. He set me down in front of an upper-class house. I rang at the front door; a servant opened. She did not need long explanations. I was expected. She led me into a room with leather-upholstered furniture and a big bureau, and gave me a blank look as she shut the door behind her. An elderly man with a grey beard came into the room and scrutinised me with steel-grey eyes through his pince-nez. I had to take off my jacket and roll up my sleeve.

A young woman came in from an adjoining room with a notepad. She greeted the professor and sat on a chair by the bureau. The professor felt the few remaining soft areas of my arm below the elbow. Although his fingers were warm, I shivered. "The arm looks positively skeletal," he said drily and glanced at the secretary, who smiled at the apt comparison. The professor cleared his throat. He was clearly pleased with his witty remark. He tested the bending and stretching capabilities of wrist and fingers.

"Can you remember on what day Dr. Hörnli cut open the plaster cast?"

"Yes. On the third day."

"You mean, the second day after the accident?"

"Yes."

"Are you quite sure of that?"

Yes. The first day after the accident he tried to do it with his penknife. But he cut the skin. The plaster got stained. So the doctor soon stopped."

"Has your father told you how to answer?"

"Why should he? I was there myself."

He chuckled into his beard.

"He doesn't believe me," I thought. Disconcerted, I looked at him. There was a peculiar expression on his face. "You don't need to be afraid of the professor," my father had told me. "Just tell him what happened. You are the one who knows it best."

"Can we begin?" asked the professor. The secretary nodded and he dictated:

"Left hand and left forearm are withered, the hand crippled. The ulna is shortened by $6\frac{1}{2}$ cm. Two finger-widths below the elbow there is a sudden extreme atrophy of soft parts and bone. The hand is almost completely paralysed, the fingers bent by contractures. There is a weak gripping capability between thumb and forefinger. The four other fingers are clawed."

I wondered why such a description was necessary. The judges had seen the arm. They knew what it looked like. The professor went on dictating, and I grew more and more agitated.

"Write: The doctor made every effort to do his best; the same evening he examined the dressing and the hand, but could not see the swelling and congestion inside the cast. When he was called by the patient's sister the next day, the ischaemia had already set in."

"That isn't what happened, Professor! We already had to call the doctor on the day of the accident. Veronika Ruden testified to that in court. And my aunt knew exactly what the fingers looked like. Cold and blue as bilberries. Karl from the store and Alfred..."

"I don't have to investigate who said what," the doctor interrupted. "I leave that to the judge. In drawing up my report I cannot be drawn into the various disagreements between the parties."

I nodded incredulously. I did not understand what he meant. It was difficult to understand him in any case, since he spoke "Baslese". A native of Valais can just about follow Berne German, but the Basle dialect is considerably more obscure. He went on:

"As Dr. Hörnli expressly emphasises, the first day after the accident he cut open the plaster cast lengthways…"

"That's not true, Professor," I interjected. This time I was firmer.

"At least let me finish the sentence! …the plaster cast lengthways, comma, though not completely. He left a ring two fingers thick at the top and bottom edges."

"But that isn't true! He tried to cut the plaster at the elbow. Just with a penknife. But it didn't work. He cut me when he tried. It would have been much harder in the middle of the cast."

"That is an assertion! – Doctor Hörnli expressly emphasises…"

"If you cut open a stove-pipe lengthways, do you start in the middle?"

"Now I've had enough. I'm not here to be instructed. Your views may interest the court – they do not interest me! I have to give an expert opinion, not carry out a cross-examination."

"But you want to find out who's guilty, don't you?"

"What I have to find out is my business. And if you interrupt me once more, I'll send you home."

That would not have been so unwelcome to me, as I was now filled with foreboding. "Why does he accept what Dr. Hörnli said?" I wondered. "We proved he was lying."

The professor briefly paced about, while he cleaned his pince-nez with his handkerchief and cleared his throat. He looked at me as if he was about to say something, then thought the better of it and asked the secretary:

"Where were we? Oh yes, of course. Herr Doktor Hörnli emphasised, and his statement is entirely believable..." And so it went on. He even seemed to me to be contradicting himself, and I involuntarily shook my head, earning further black looks from the obstinate gentleman.

"Write the following, Fraulein: The patient has now grown into a tall youth, is strongly built and in a good state of health." And somewhat later:

"Nor is it impossible that a certain lack of resistance to infection in sickly childhoood played a part."

I was back outside the house. The professor's examination had confused me utterly. I did not even know from which direction I had arrived in the taxi. I heard the noise of a tram in the distance. Its bell rang intermittently. I went off in that direction. Suddenly I was standing in a big square. A dark-green tram drew up and stopped in front of me. Although I did not know where it was going, I tried to get on. The door was open, but blocked in the middle by a horizontal bar. I tried to get under the bar into the tram. The conductor kept pushing me back. The more energetically I tried to climb on, the harder he pushed, shouting something at me that I didn't understand. A lady tugged at my sleeve:

"We have to get in on the other side. Come on, my young friend."

I smiled awkwardly and followed her. The conductor was still grumbling: "These country bumpkins shouldn't be let loose until they've learnt how to ride in a tram!" I sat down with a red face. Opposite me were two schoolboys of my age. They had brown leather satchels under their arms and were laughing, having seem my efforts to board the tram. The one with the fringe said, loudly enough to be heard by other people:

"The little kid's had his trouser legs sawn off."

His friend giggled. I looked down at my three-quarter length trousers and swung my high-sided shoes. At the next stop I had to get out and take the tram that went in the opposite direction.

I reached Zermatt on the last train that night. Father was waiting for me at the station. He was curious. Even before I could greet him he asked:

"How did it go in Basle?"

"Not well."

"Why?"

"The old doctor didn't believe a word I said. The only thing that counted was Dr. Hörnli's pack of lies. But I told him to his face."

"I hope you weren't rude to him?"

"Not rude. But I..."

"For heaven's sake, you didn't argue with him, did you?"

"No, of course not!"

"That's all right then. I told you how important that man can be for us. People like him must be handled with kid gloves."

"I'd better not say any more. Otherwise it'll be my fault if it all goes wrong."

"It can't go wrong! We've got right on our side. Think of all the witnesses!"

We walked up the main street. People looked at us curiously. When we reached the "Valais Arms", Father said.

"Come on, Hannes, let's have a drink together. I'm sure it'll help you look on the bright side, like your father." He laughed roguishly. He put his hand on my shoulder and we went into the inn together. Father ordered half a bottle of Fendant. Some older men sat down at our table. They agreed with Father that the doctor should be punished by law for his bungling. He'd have to cough up a few thousand, all right. Father ordered another half bottle of Fendant and a few glasses.

Disillusion

We sat a long time around the table. Mother cleared away the gruel, cheese and rye bread. Father did not want to eat. When he came back from the court, we were already at the kitchen table. From his tired steps on the stairs and landing we concluded that he had been drowning his sorrows. He came in with dragging feet. Mother stood at the stove. We knew that our case had not gone well.

For a moment Father paused in the doorway. His lined face was shaded by his hat. The only electric lamp glowed on the table. He was not drunk. Not in the least. "Come on in," said Mother gently. He looked at her mutely. Then he nodded several time, as if she had asked him a question.

"Well, come on," she repeated. He went up to her and embraced her passionately.

This was unusual. Father had never come home like this before. It was not like him to be silent. What he had on his chest he always said at once. Usually louder than we liked. Oaths were liable to fly, Italian ones in particularly annoying cases. Now he came hesitantly and silently through the door. His face was towards the stove. He had his arms round Mother, and his shoulders shook. Was he crying?

We put our spoons down. I could not remember ever having seen Father cry. My little brothers and I kept quiet, so impressed we were, and close to tears. Only the burning wood crackled in the stove. And above our heads my uncle tramped around his kitchen. After a while Mother said:

"Please, sit down. And eat something."

"No, I don't want to eat!" But he sat down with us. There could be no doubt that the case had gone badly. Gradually it came out. In fragments. Then he grew heated. His voice got louder. His blue eyes gleamed. He was again the Father we knew. He banged the table with his fist. The aluminium plates clattered. My youngest brother started to cry. Mother took him on her lap.

"The humiliating thing is that we can't even get a verdict!"

"Can't get a verdict?" Mother did not understand.

"We've got to drop the bloody claim!"

"You won't do that, will you, Father?" I put in.

"I have to! The report from that miserable Professor Riklin in Basle is so damning for us…"

The words stuck in his throat. "We have no chance. None at all. Our lawyer says so."

"Then let the judges pass their judgement and answer for it before God!" Mother retorted.

"And I'll have to bear the legal costs. Hörnli's as well!"

"But the judges know the doctor lied. They'll realise we can't believe everything the Basle doctor says," I suggested.

"A lot you know about it! That scrap of paper suits the Visp people down to the ground."

"But Professor Matti is a distinguished man as well," Mother objected.

"His report says that the plaster cast was the cause of everything."

"Anything that went against Hörnli, Riklin simply ignored. It didn't suit him. Doctors are like crows. They won't peck each other's eyes out."

"I just wonder what we've got judges for."

"In this country you've got to have the right friends or the belong to the right party, then you'll always come out on top. That's how it is. It's damnably sad, but true."

"Shouldn't you let the Governor know – our friend in Berne? Perhaps he can help us," Mother suggested.

"Didn't I tell you?"

"No. What?"

"The lawyer gave me a letter from the Governor. Where have I got it?"

He looked in his breast pocket.

"Here. You won't believe it. He's one of the top people in the country, after all. Listen to what he writes! Father put on his wire-framed glasses, looked at Mother and me over the lenses and read, while the paper trembled in his hand. He underlined the most important passages by stretching out his legs with their nailed boots, or scraping them back to his chair. He always did that when he was agitated.

Dear Sir,

Taugwalder has sent me your letter and the report of Professor Riklin.

Professor Matti takes issue with various points in the report and has the impression it is based on incorrect assumptions. It is certainly open to criticism on the grounds that no witnesses were questioned and that the facts are either not recorded or unreliably recorded. Despite all that, it now seems to me that the case is in an unfavourable position. A bitter injustice is being done to Taugwalder, and in comparison to other cases I have heard of, one can only wonder at the report and the outcome of the trial. E. Sch.

Again, there was a ghostly silence in our kitchen. Father put the letter back into his pocket.

"The lawyer advises us to settle the matter amicably, so that Dr. Hörnli at least has to pay his own costs. That's how it looks. Even the Governor can't do anything."

"Whatever did that Basle professor write?" asked Mother angrily.

"A supreme medical-legal report! 28 pages long! About everything except what he should have written. A whole litany of distinguished professors: Hildebrand, Zuppinger, Christen and whatever they are called. All of them people who have never seen my boy and have never had anything to do with our case. Whereas our Professor Matti, who took the poor boy over in his pitiable state and knew the case inside-out, was ignored!"

"But the court can't possibly accept that!" Mother could not believe such a thing could happen.

"They want to hang us with the Riklin report. The lawyer said so. I've got a summary of it on me. Here it is."

He again took his spectacles from their dark sheath, hooked the two wires behind his ears and read:

Summary.

In the supreme expert's opinion the fate of the injured forearm of the plaintiff Taugwalder was really predetermined, both by the uncommon nature of the injury and by what might be called the inevitable misdiagnosis and the resulting inappropriate but not incorrect choice of treatment by circular distraction plaster cast. On the medical grounds established above the supreme expert cannot find evidence of any malpractice, negligence or other culpable omission.

Professor Rilkin

I felt choked, suffocated by our helplessness.

"I'll murder that damned Hörnli!"

Father suddenly grew very calm. "What did you say, Hannes? I never want to hear you say that again. Never! Do you understand?"

"He's a damned liar!"

"He certainly is. But no-one has the right to try to take someone else's life! Give him a thrashing – yes, that's all right. But I'll take care of that."

The conversation was making Mother uneasy. "Come on, you two little marmots, it's your bedtime. You're falling asleep all over my table." She took my two little brothers to the bedroom.

I stayed behind with Father. I knew I had said something stupid. I felt ashamed. Father kept silent. He was glowering at the kitchen table. From time to time he sighed, stretched his legs or pulled them back under his chair. He was probably working out how to give the doctor a hiding. without witnesses being present.

After a while Mother came back into the kitchen. She busied herself at the stove. Now and then she passed the back of her hand across her mouth, to wipe some words that remained unsaid from her lips. My sister was no longer at home. She had taken a housekeeping job with a family that ran a sawmill in Sion, to learn French. She complained of homesickness. She said she constantly had to carry heavy boards about and had hardly a chance to talk to anyone. Mother did not think this was right and asked Father to write to the family. She hung the copper pan on the wall. Countless glowing specks shone like stars on its hot sooty underside. Clusters of them went out, vanished, then lit up again. Mother was sunk in her thoughts. At the convent she had bridled at the idea of bearing injustice in humility, but life had taught her how to do it. "I wanted you to learn a proper profession," said Father. "And now... devil take it..."

"I like being a lift-boy. They'll take me back at the Hotel Monte Rosa. I like it there."

Father went on brooding. He took a deep breath. Otherwise all was still in the kitchen. After a while he asked Mother to brew a strong coffee. Some of the words stuck in his throat.

We want to help

On the sunny side of the valley, I was looking after our cow and the two goats. The pasture was in a larch wood near a rocky outcrop as high as a house. Over thousands of years the rock had been split and turned into a shepherds' climbing warren.

On the shady side of the valley, in the Aroleid-woods, I heard from time to time the thud of an axe and the rasp of a hand saw. Father was digging up tree stumps for firewood. My sister and younger brother were helping him. My sister had come back prematurely from her housekeeping job in Sion. Homesickness had been too much for her.

Now and then the crash of an explosion broke the autumn stillness and reverberated through the valley. A wisp of blue smoke rose from the larch branches and dispersed itself into the clear air. Fahter no longer allowed me to help him with heavy work. I had scraped the skin of my hand while digging and splitting wood, and my parents feared a new infection.

I had to get used to being unable to do all jobs. Simple things like pushing a wheelbarrow or milking were now beyond me. To hold a nail in one hand and wield the hammer in the other took patient practice. I had to relearn simple tasks such as tying my shoelaces with much gnashing of teeth.

I was sent to the pasture with the cow and the goats. We only had one cow left. We had had sell Stärri when we got the bill for our legal costs. When our neighbour Max led the cow out of our stable, we all cried.

I had lost my ability to talk with the mountains. Looking back, I seemed to have been indulging in empty, high-flown words. I had every reason to look up at the mountains with bowed head, through my eyelashes. They cheerfully bore the deep-blue sky on their whitewashed shoulders and no longer took any notice of me. I was tempted to climb the big rock and try out all the routes I had mastered before my accident. The result was that I was soon lying on my back beside the rock with torn trousers and grazed knees. I rolled up my trouser legs to expose the knees to the sun. A scab soon formed over the raw spots.

An elderly gentleman and a lady came up the shepherd's path through the wood. It was a path not used by strangers, as it only led to the pasture. Holiday-makers were rare at this time of year. I assumed they must have lost their way and wanted to save them a further climb:

"It's straight along the bottom to Zmutt!" I called to them. They stopped, exchanged a few words, and then continued up the path. The cow, too, watched the two strangers as they approached. I rolled down my trouser legs and awaited their arrival.

"We're not going to Zmutt," said the man.

"This path doesn't lead anywhere. There are only rocks that way," I returned.

"We've come to see you. You're Hannes, aren't you?"

I pulled a face and looked at the man suspiciously. He was wearing a weather-beaten hat in the mountain farmer's style, had bushy eyebrows above alert, piercing eyes, and his grey moustache was slightly discoloured from smoking. He was breathing heavily. The climb had taken its toll. Behind him came the lady, showing a kindly, pointed face with slightly screwed-up blue eyes. She hid her grey hair under a white summer hat. Now they stood beside me. The way they spoke German suggested they were Dutch.

"Your mother told us we could find you here. We had tea with her," the gentleman began.

"Aha," I thought, "two more nosey people who want to see my arm. When will Mother stop whining to all and sundry?"

"My name is de Bruyn. This is my wife."

"Hello, Hannes," said the lady in her Dutch accent.

"We'd like to talk to you," the man went on.

I thought: You don't need to say that, you just do it. My mistrust grew.

"My wife and I would like to help you," said the man.

"Help me?" I repeated, surprised. Perhaps they are bored with hiking for days on end or sitting at the hotel. So they would like to help me mind the cow for a change?

"I don't need any help!" I was quite rude.

"Really?" The man laughed awkwardly.

"Your mother is worried about your future," said the lady. "I'm a lift-boy – in summer." "That's fine," said the man. "But soon you'll be a man. And then what? Or do you always want to be a yokel?"

What does he mean by calling me a yokel? Why doesn't he leave me in peace?

"Shall we sit down and chat a little?" suggested the lady.

Perhaps they really didn't want to see my arm. I began to open up. We sat down on the grass beside the climbing rock. They didn't say any more about wanting to help, which suited me. I was asked to tell them the names of the flowers growing beside the rock; and where the stream we could hear rushing in the valley below went to. I was able to tell them a lot of news about the capital of our country, the minster, the bridges and monuments. Then the lady said:

"My husband has heard about a clinic that has developed new apparatus for making immovable limbs better."

"I'm never going back to hospital."

"It's not a hospital," the man interjected.

"It's an institute. It's called the Balgrist Institute. And the marvellous thing about it is that you can go to school while you are having the treatment. Secondary school, too."

That may well be, I thought, but it doesn't interest me. Why are they telling me all this? There was a moment of silence. No-one said anything. Then I repeated:

"I spent a long time in hospital."

"Yes, we heard about it." It was the lady who said this.

"And about the business with the doctor. The judge did not do a good job."

"We lost the case. Father had to sell a cow. Now we've only got that one left."

"Yes, the doctor did a miserable job," said the man.

"And he lied! He lied!" I was getting heated.

It was good to find oneself understood. In Zermatt, opinions were divided about the doctor. The circles close to the priest and the parish chairman claimed he was a good doctor. Our relations and the families who had already had dealings with the doctor had not a good word to say for him.

"We're friends of your mother," said the lady. "We have no children and we should like to do something for you."

"And we're not completely penniless," joked the man.

The way he said it made me smile in spite of myself. I nodded shyly in assent. We chatted for a while. "How strange life is," I thought. "You battle for months with people who will do anything, however bad, to evade their responsibilities. And then you suddenly have people in front of you who you have never seen in your life, and they say: 'We want to help you.'"

The man pulled a gold watch from his pocket.

"We must be on our way. You'll hear from us again soon." Without further ado he shook my hand and left. The lady looked at me kindly.

"Give your mother our best wishes. Goodbye!" She held out her hand to me. She had long, delicate fingers. I couldn't think of anything sensible to say, and for a moment I held her hand, looking gratefully up at her. She came a step closer and kissed me on the forehead.

Standing between the climbing rock and a juniper bush, I looked after the couple as they followed the path down through the wood. Once they stopped, turned and waved with their walking sticks.

"I must tell my parents," I thought. I rounded up the animals before the usual time and set off for home. Only now did I notice how painful my knees were. That evening my mother surprised us with a wonderful polenta. She had spread a baking tin with butter, poured in boiled maize an put it in the oven to bake. What emerged from the oven was the most glorious, golden "Gugelhopf."

Father loved dried polenta with cheese above all else. He drank coffee with it. We children poured cold milk on to the hot maize and ate it with gusto. Even Father kept saying: "Goodness, I'm hungry," and the wrinkles fanned affably between his eyes and ears. Mother pushed the dish towards him:

"Help yourself. It's there to be eaten."

Above the table the paraffin lamp flickered behind a big, milky shade. To save fuel, Father was apt to turn down the wick to give a meagre light. Today he had allowed a proper flame. The soft light shed on our faces a glow of security and hope.

Leavetaking

In October the valley was bathed in the gentle warmth of the autumn sun. At night the frost nipped the slightly yellowing grass, in which were a few forgotten meadow saffrons and cowslips. In the early morning there was rime on the grass, and in shady hollows the puddles shielded themselves with a thin layer of ice, which crackled under our feet.

The first winter snow had fallen on the mountains, which shone dazzlingly against a deep blue sky, but the lower slopes were still rust-brown. Larches tinted the edge of the forest yellow-gold, and the bilberry bushes covered whole stretches of ground in glowing wine-red.

By midday the sun had melted the frost in the valley. The farmers led out their herds into the fields. They were tied to posts in the meadows by long chains. When the grass within their reach had been neatly nibbled down, they were allotted a new patch to graze. The thud of mallets on the pegs and the jangling of bells could be heard all around. It was the eve of my departure. Mother put out my clothes ready for me. From time to time she tried out a song. She always sang when she was sad.

Mr. de Bruyn had organised everything for me at Balgrist. The Zurich school authorities were prepared to try me out at secondary school for a few weeks to see if I could catch up my lost schooling.

In a few days the railway was to end its summer service. Father was happy that everything had been arranged in time and that I would be able to travel down the valley by train. A nurse was to meet me at Zurich station. I was to hold a copy of the Schweizer Illustrierte conspicuously in my hand so that she could recognise me.

"You must say goodbye to the priest and the teacher," Mother advised. That was what young people normally did.

"The priest? No. I'm not saying goodbye to him."

"He didn't mean any harm," Mother urged.

"I don't know what he meant, but I know what he said."

After a while she said: "Well, at least go to the teacher and Aunt Apollonia. And bring me some salt and maize from the village store."

That I did. I met the teacher in his flat by the Triftbach. During the summer months when the school was closed he worked as manager at the Hotel Zermatterhof. He was surprised to hear that I was going to try for secondary school. "You hardly attended school at all during the last two winters. They make big demands on you at secondary school. It won't be easy for you," he warned. He believed he owed it to his profession to send me on my way with a piece of good advice:

"There are all kinds of dangers lying in wait in the city. Be careful! Never go to dancing classes. That's been the ruin of many a young person. You get to know fast girls and could easily find yourself in trouble.

I promised him not to go to dancing classes so that I wouldn't meet any fast girls. Then I went down the stone steps to the street and put my hat back on. Aunt Apollonia was a widow. She had an apartment in a house on the church square.

"All the young people are leaving us," she said thoughtfully. "If you go to the station these days, you see them getting on the trains with their cases. They're all looking for work. And when they've found it, they marry and stay where they are. Four of my children have married women from other parts. I don't see them often."

"I'll come back," I assured her.

"That's what mine said, and I still had to give them up. Your mother will lose you too."

She opened the kitchen window, and from the wire-mesh box hanging outside in the fresh shade that served as a refrigerator she took a fine apple.

"You can't blame anyone for staying where their bread's buttered. Who's going to find work here in winter? We live at the end of the world."

In the letter-box of our Zermatt apartment there were a number of newspapers and a letter addressed to me. A grey envelope with a magenta lining. Quite upper-class. Sister Klara wrote to tell me that she was giving up nursing and going to stay with friends in Santander. She needed to get away from everything so that she could put her life back together. I did not know what to make of all this. Who were these friends in Santander? She had never talked about them. And why did she have to get away from everything? What was the matter with her? She had been such a cheerful nurse. I didn't understand. With Father's papers and the salt and maize in my rucksack, the letter, which I stuffed into my pocket, and Aunt Apollonia's apple, I sauntered back to Zumsee.

Father was chopping firewood in front of the house. When he saw me, he put the axe aside and sat on the steps.

"Are you finding it hard to take your leave of us?" he asked.

"Yes. Who likes going to a strange place?"

"I can understand that. But we haven't got much here," he replied. "The work is hard and brings in very little money. It's true, you're your own master, and what you earn comes from your own land: milk, rye, potatoes... It's not much, but you can live off it."

I nodded: "I would have liked to help."

"I know, son. We've just been unlucky. We mustn't lose heart. We must always look for new opportunities.

I gave him the papers and went to Mother. She was packing my clothes, which were neatly stacked on the bed, into a case. One of its catches didn't work. She said:

"Everything's breaking here these days."

She wasn't very talkative. Something was weighing on her mind. She was lost in her thoughts. Suddenly she said:

"For next summer I urgently need a new table and some chairs. I can't serve the guests tea on the tree-trunks that are lying around. And I really ought to have a wardrobe at last."

I nodded. Why is she telling me this? I have my own worries.

"You could ask Father to make the furniture this winter."

"I could? Why me?"

"He likes you, and listens to you. I've often asked him, but he doesn't listen to me. He likes to take life too easily. The wood has been lying there for ages, but he doesn't touch it. He really could do a bit more work."

"I can't say to Father: I'm off now. See that you work a bit harder and get on with making the table and chairs."

"Why not? It just depends on how you say it."

"But he's my father! And he's quite old... and disabled."

"He doesn't need to work all day on it. Just a bit every day. He likes working like that. He's not too tired to do other things."

"But Mother, you must understand that I can't order him to do this or that."

"Did I say anything about ordering?" Mother took the two shirts out of the case and put in my second suit. She was upset.

"I'm only asking you to tell him to make the things for me. I really do need them.

Is that asked too much?»

"Stop it now, Mother. I simply can't. I can't do that to my father."

"What about me? You let me do everything! No-one asks me whether I can manage or not."

"Why can't you understand? It just isn't possible."

"Then don't do it," she said and went into the kitchen. I think she was crying. I waited a short while, then followed her. She was bustling about the wood-stove. I tried to come back to our conversation. But she did not want to.

"Can't you leave me alone now? You can see I've things to do. In the end, I'm the one who does everything."

"Father was chopping wood outside."

"You probably agree with him that it's just one of my whims and I could serve the guests just as well sitting on a stone or on the grass."

"No, of course I don't. But I want to keep out of it."

"Then please do keep out of it. But leave me in peace," she sobbed. "Now I know where I stand."

I didn't know what else I could say. Whatever was the matter with Mother? I had never seen her like this. I was totally confused. I went out on to the veranda and tramped down the stairs. Hardly was I out of the house when I felt angry at the way I had behaved. When Father caught sight of me, he leant the axe against the wall. He sat down on the stairs, pulled his pipe from his pocket and stuffed it with his strong tobacco. I think he would have liked to chat with me. But I was too upset and wandered off between the houses towards the well. I was angry: "Just when I'm about to leave, I have to quarrel with Mother. How stupid! I haven't even time to make it up with her. Why should I be the one to tell Father: Get on with it, make up the chairs and table. He must have a reason why he hasn't started yet. It's just impossible. And tomorrow I have to go away. What a mess!"

In the meadow behind the huts my younger brother was looking after a sheep that had recently given birth to two lambs. The little creatures were still very unsteady on their stiff legs. They tried to gambol, but had difficulty keeping their balance. Rudolf pressed a lamb to his chest and stroked its soft, curly wool. He was a shepherd who loved animals. The joy he took in the lamb shone from his eyes.

When he saw me, he let the lamb go. It hopped to its mother and sought the udder with frantic nudges. As it sucked, it showed its small, red tongue, with which it pressed the teats. The mother sniffed at the lamb to make sure it had the proper stable smell. The lamb wagged its tail and sucked greedily.

When I got home with Rudolf, Father was sitting over his papers at the table. Mother served a platter of roast potatoes. She called the dish "délice valaisanne". The potatoes were covered in the pan with slices of cheese. A lid on the pan made sure that the cheese melted into a liquid mass. Sprinkled with pepper, the potato cake was served in the pan.

I had no opportunity for the exchange of words with Mother that was so urgent. "But I have to make it up with her! I can't leave like this!"

"Maybe Father will go to Lauber Fenner's after dinner," I thought. The old men of Zumsee often met there for a game of cards. Fenner no longer had any young children. He lived as a widower with his unmarried daughter in a comfortable apartment. Though Father sometimes complained that Fenner turned his paraffin lamp so low that you could hardly see the cards, he was always eager to go. They played with old cards with pictures of Death, a giant and a naked lady. They called the game "troggen" (from Tarot).

But this evening Father stayed home.

"Let's be together for once," he said. However, he soon began to get restless. He went to the window and looked over at the lighted windows of Fenner's house. His friends were there, playing cards. Father sat under the lamp on the corner seat and dug the jass cards out of the drawer. This was a challenge. My sister, my younger brother and I liked playing jass with him.

Father and I were usually on opposite sides. Neither he nor I could shuffle and deal the cards easily. We let our partner do it when it was our turn. I played with my sister and he with my younger brother.

Father could hold the cards skilfully in his left hand although the fingers were missing. I pushed them between my forefinger and thumb. It sometimes happened in the heat of the game that one or other of us dropped our cards. We had to pick them up and rearrange them. The other players would either be tolerant or make a witty remark.

Mother had finished the washing up. She came into the living room and sat down on a stool with us at the table. While she patched shirts and socks in the weak light, she chatted with us. She borrowed Father's glasses to thread her needle. I kept glancing at her over my cards. She avoided my eyes and concentrated on her mending. When I said goodnight, I embraced her longer than usual. She let me do it, but I felt a certain reserve.

The next day I had to leave. Father carried my little case with the umbrella tied to it. Mother wanted to accompany us as far as the chapel at Blatten. On the rise, from which you could get a last view of the Zermatt Valley, we stopped for a moment. The grey slate roofs of the village rose in tiers. Blue woodsmoke curled from the chimneys. The stream that flowed along the bottom of the valley reflected the morning gleam of the mountains, over which the sunlight was spreading. I stole a last glance at the Matterhorn, slightly embarrassed, as one turns towards someone when one is ashamed. Father noticed it. He took off his hat. We stood there silently, and Mother cried. Then we went on, each sunk in his own thoughts. Before Mother went into the chapel, she said goodbye to me. She did it quickly, as she wanted to be brave. Father and I went on down the valley.

Aunt Apollonia was right. Like so many young people who left the mountains at that time to find work in the towns I too stayed in foreign parts. My birth certificate was lodged now here, now there, in a town-hall file.

I never returned to my valley.

But my thoughts are drawn back constantly to my homeland. To the lost valley.

My grandparents, Peter and Katharina Taugwalder-Lauber, with their eleven children. Our daily bread was thinly sliced. With one exception, all the sons became mountain guides, and with one exception, all the daughters married mountain guides. The mountain dominated all, demanding courage, pride and love.

My parents, Rudolf and Barbara Taugwalder-Z'Brunn, with their children during the difficult years of the First World War. Alfons and Lina standing, Father with his arm round Rudolf and Emil on his knee. Hannes beside his mother.

My parents Rudolf and Barbara soon after their marriage, working as hotel porter and chambermaid in Menton. At that time there was no paid employment in Zermatt in winter. Father found hotel work hard-going.

My parents towards the end of their lives, in the little garden beside their apartment in Zermatt. The missing fingers on Father Rudolf's left hand are visible; he lost them through frost-bite on the first ascent of the north face of the Huascaran.

Mother Barbara at the living-room window of our flat in «Zum See». She had a friendly greeting ready for passing hikers, and was very glad if they stopped for refreshments. She badly needed the income.

Top: On the high pasture at Kalbermatten. Lina, Karolina and Hannes in front of the door to the kitchen and bedroom of the wooden cabin. Rudolf busy eating on the ladder leading to the hayloft.

Centre: After the infamous court case the family had only one cow left. Rudolf and Hannes as the happy shepherds. One of the young goats insisted on being in the picture.

Bottom left: When Hannes could still dream of being a mountain guide. With his godmother and her husband Baron Collot d'Escury on the summit of the Riffelhorn.

Bottom right: After the accident and the medical mistreatment Hannes wanted to become a painter, which did not accord with his father's ideas.

Hannes at four months, dressed up for the photographer.

Group portrait in front of the tea-room in «Zum See». Rudolf, the mountain guide Aufdenblatten, our Dutch godmother with Emil on her knee, Lina standing behind Hannes, who was carrying his godmother's rucksack on an excursion.

Hannes as a lift-boy after his accident, with employees of the Hotel Monte Rosa

The rock with the pine that fought doggedly for survival and was only recently uprooted by a storm. While tending the herd, Hannes liked to sit on this rock dreaming and gazing into the sky until he was overcome with longing for distant places.

The rudimentary cabin in which the summer on the pasture was spent in its present state. When it threatended to collapse under the weight of snow, the council of «Burgers» took some makeshift counter-measures.

The Kalbermatten pasture with new buildings. Today hikers are offered a generous meal. Earlier they had to make do with milk, hard bread and cheese.

The valley that the young shepherd-boy Hannes had to leave to earn his living in foreign parts. His lost valley, lost too because much of the lightheartedness an kindness of its poor inhabitants has disappeared as conditions have changed.

Hannes at the age of four wanted to become a mountain guide.

Mother Barbara happy to be able to serve English guests with a good cup of tea.